CALIFORNIA

McDougal Littell

MATH
Course 1

Larson   Boswell   Kanold   Stiff

Notetaking Guide

The Notetaking Guide contains a lesson-by-lesson framework that allows students to take notes on and review the main concepts of each lesson in the textbook. Each Notetaking Guide lesson features worked-out examples and guided practice exercises similar to those found in the textbook. The Notetaking Guide also provides graphic organizer templates for students to use when taking notes or doing homework.

McDougal Littell
A DIVISION OF HOUGHTON MIFFLIN COMPANY
Evanston, Illinois • Boston • Dallas

ISBN 10: 0-618-89307-5
ISBN 13: 978-0-618-89307-2

56789 0956 12 11 10 09

Contents

Course 1 Notetaking Guide

Graphic Organizers for Notetaking Skills Exercises

1 Number Patterns and Fractions

2 Fraction and Decimal Operations

Program Overview

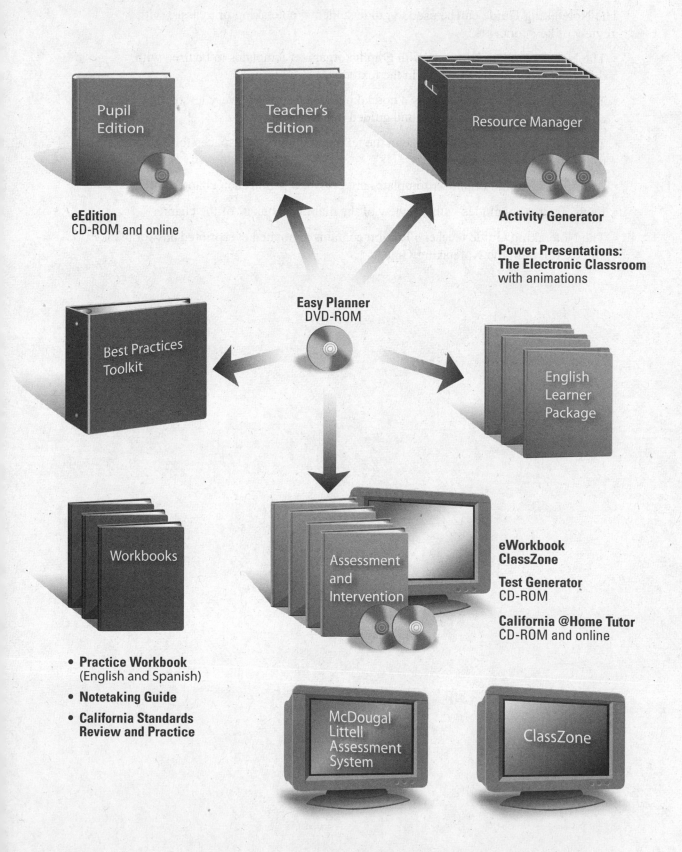

Pupil Edition

eEdition
CD-ROM and online

Teacher's Edition

Resource Manager

Activity Generator

Power Presentations:
The Electronic Classroom
with animations

Best Practices Toolkit

Easy Planner
DVD-ROM

English Learner Package

Workbooks

- **Practice Workbook**
  (English and Spanish)
- **Notetaking Guide**
- **California Standards**
  Review and Practice

Assessment and Intervention

eWorkbook
ClassZone

Test Generator
CD-ROM

California @Home Tutor
CD-ROM and online

McDougal Littell Assessment System

ClassZone

Notetaking Guide Overview

The Notetaking Guide can be used to guide students' notetaking or to assist with review of key concepts.

- The Notetaking Guide begins with graphic organizer templates to be used with the Notetaking Skills exercises in the textbook.

- These templates are followed by a notetaking framework for every lesson that contains instruction, examples, and guided practice exercises.

- The examples are similar to those in the textbook and include spaces for students to fill-in some of the steps.

- Additional graphic organizer templates are provided within each chapter.

- Each chapter concludes with a review of the main vocabulary of the chapter.

- The Notetaking Guide teacher's Edition contains annotated overprinted answer blanks and exercises in the Notetaking Guide.

Word Triangle

For use with Notetaking Skills exercise on p. 4

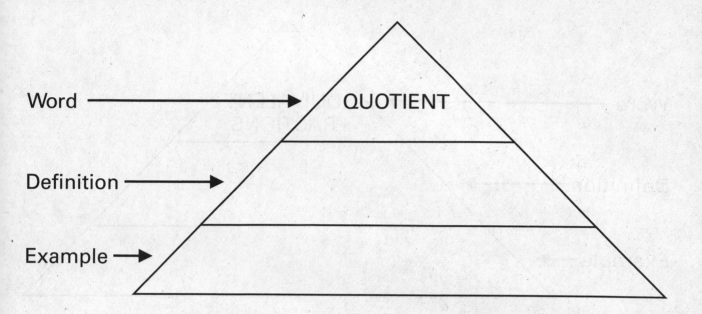

Word ———————→ QUOTIENT

Definition ———————→

Example ———→

Word Triangle

For use with Notetaking Skills exercise on p. 18

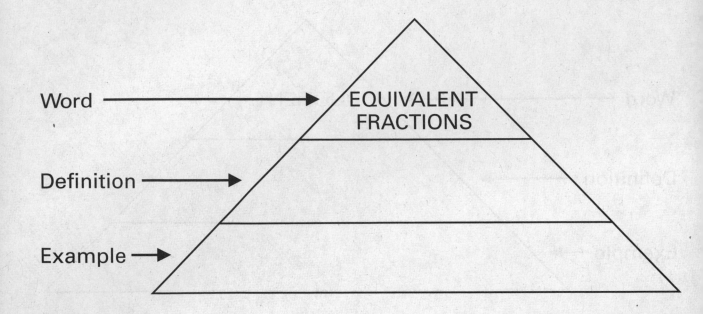

Word ⟶ EQUIVALENT FRACTIONS

Definition ⟶

Example ⟶

Word Triangle

For use with Notetaking Skills exercise on p. 56

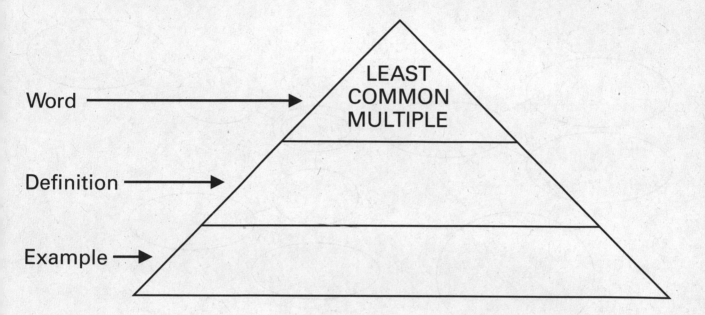

Word ⟶

Definition ⟶

Example ⟶

LEAST
COMMON
MULTIPLE

Concept Map

For use with Notetaking Skills exercise on p. 68

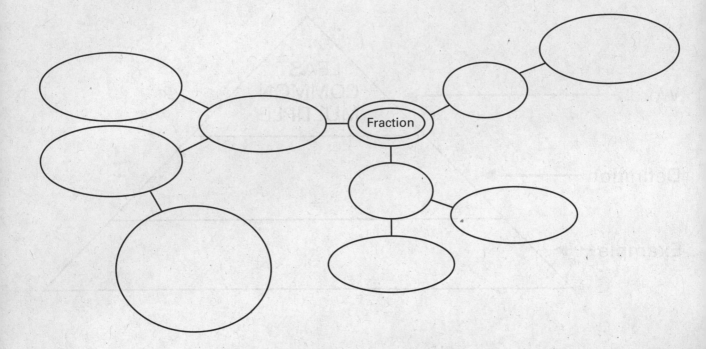

Fraction

Concept Map

For use with Notetaking Skills exercise on p. 71

Expression

Concept Map

For use with Notetaking Skills exercise on p. 117

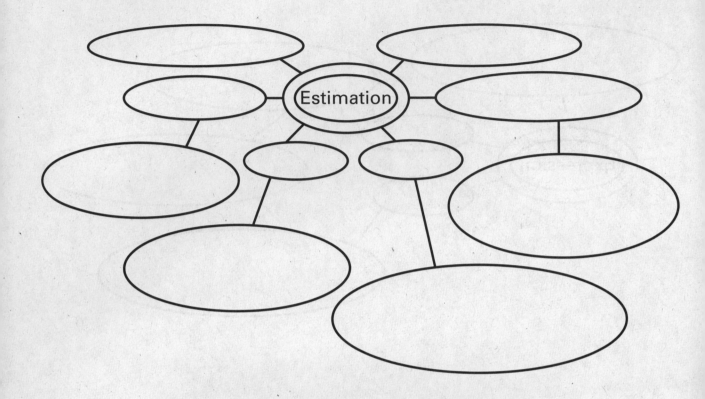

Estimation

Process Diagram

For use with Notetaking Skills exercise on p. 128

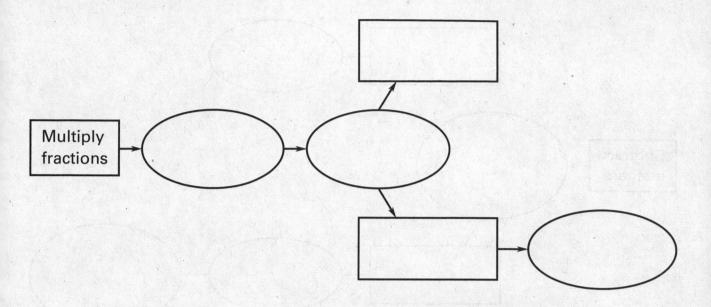

Process Diagram

For use with Notetaking Skills exercise on p. 138

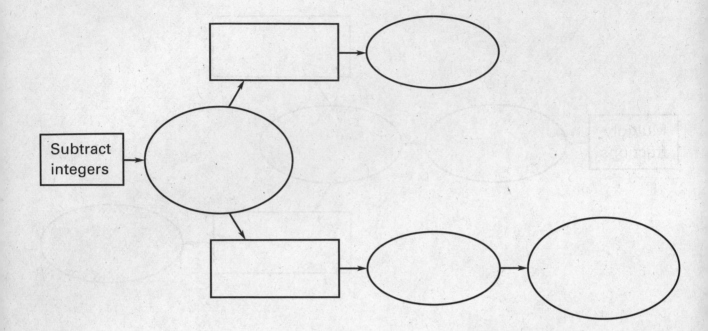

Process Diagram

For use with Notetaking Skills exercise on p. 182

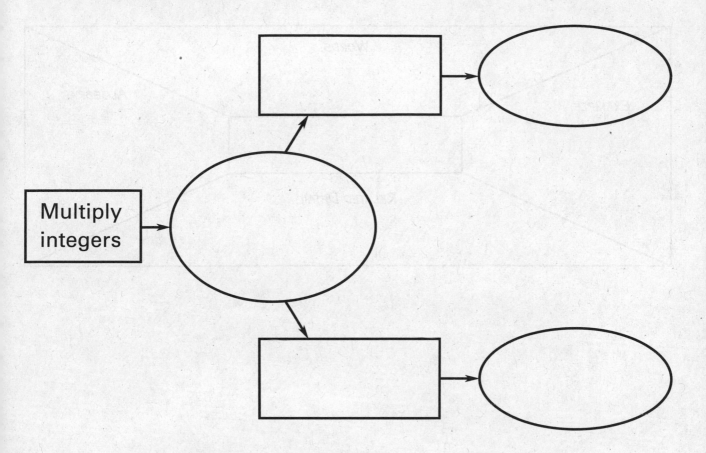

Information Frame

For use with Notetaking Skills exercise on p. 196

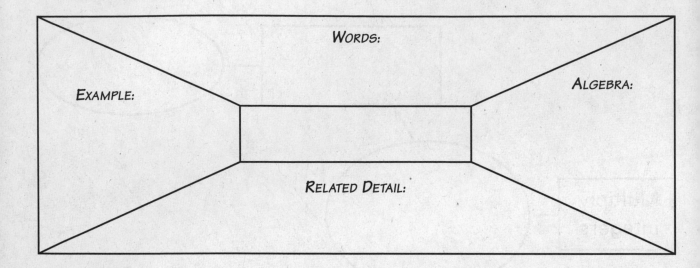

WORDS:

EXAMPLE:

ALGEBRA:

RELATED DETAIL:

Information Frame

For use with Notetaking Skills exercise on p. 236

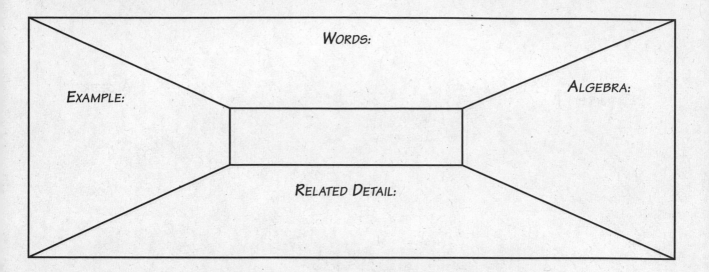

WORDS:

EXAMPLE:

ALGEBRA:

RELATED DETAIL:

Information Frame

For use with Notetaking Skills exercise on p. 243

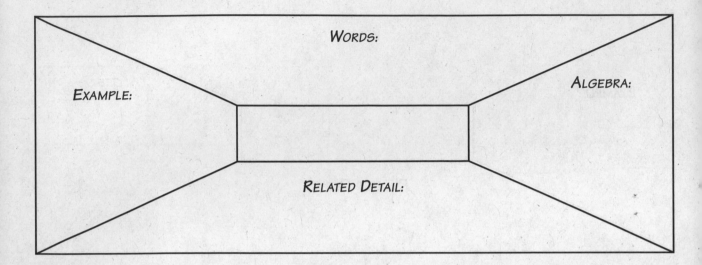

WORDS:

EXAMPLE:

ALGEBRA:

RELATED DETAIL:

Word Magnet

For use with Notetaking Skills exercise on p. 254

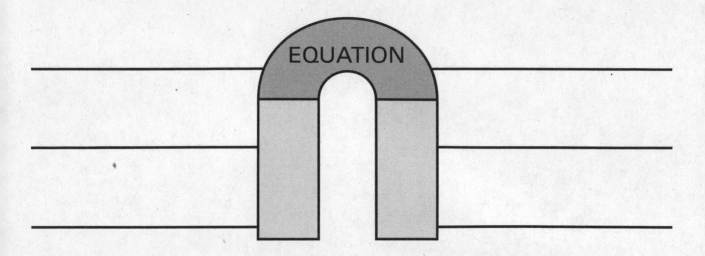

Word Magnet

For use with Notetaking Skills exercise on p. 276

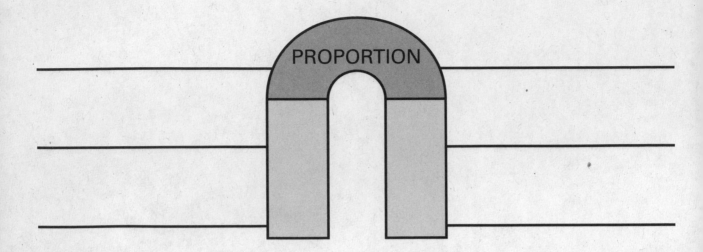

Word Magnet

For use with Notetaking Skills exercise on p. 290

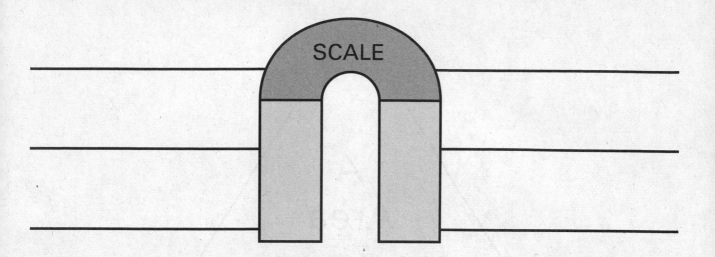

Formula Triangle

For use with Notetaking Skills exercise on p. 300

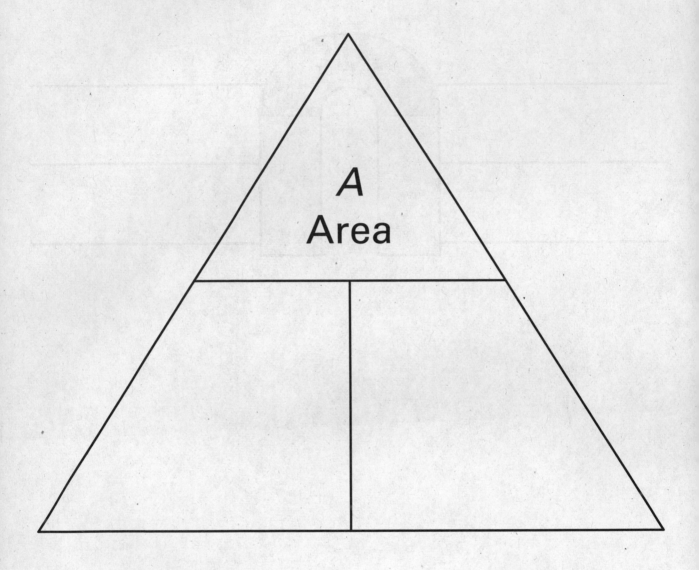

Formula Triangle

For use with Notetaking Skills exercise on p. 327

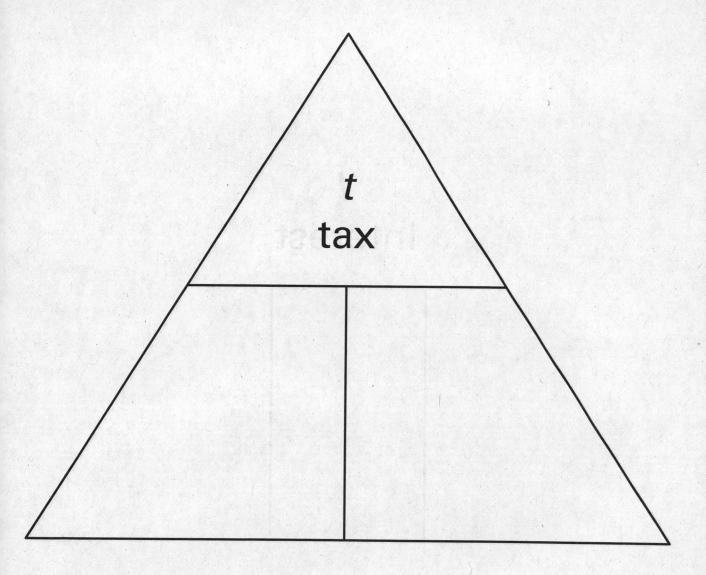

Formula Triangle

For use with Notetaking Skills exercise on p. 339

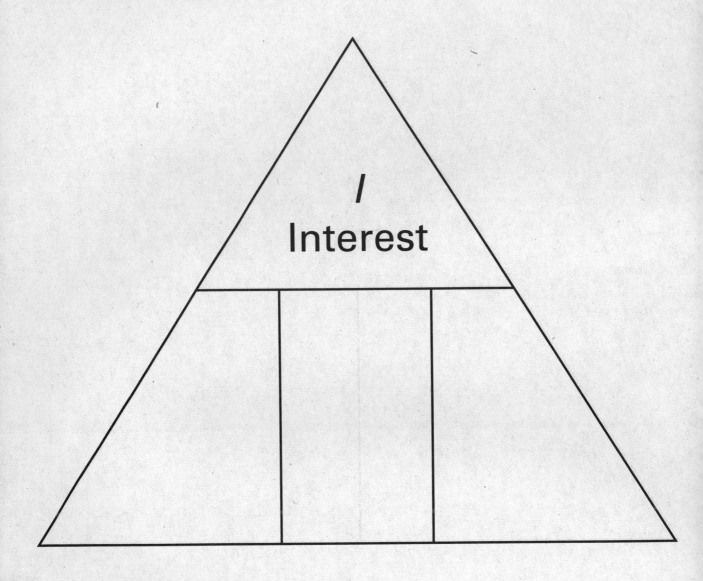

Notetaking Organizer

For use with Notetaking Skills exercise on p. 352

Write important vocabulary in the narrow column.

Write your notes in the wide column.

Write your questions at the bottom of the page.

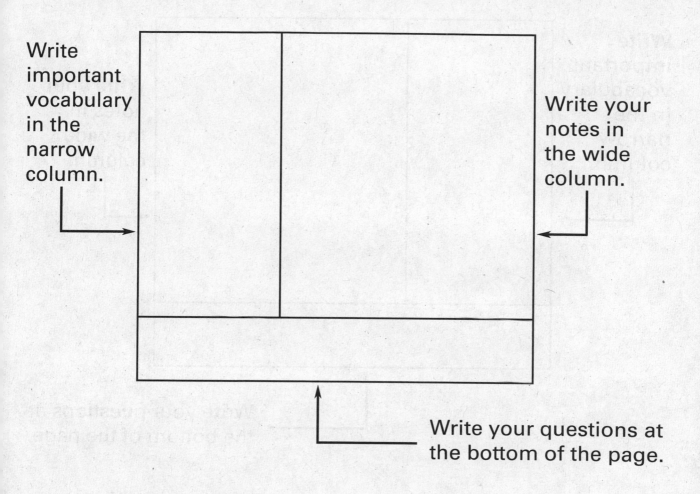

Notetaking Organizer

For use with Notetaking Skills exercise on p. 395

Write important vocabulary in the narrow column.

Write your notes in the wide column.

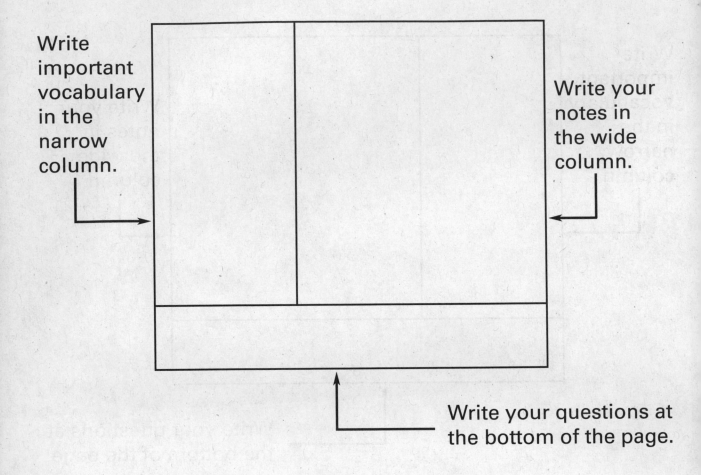

Write your questions at the bottom of the page.

Notetaking Organizer

For use with Notetaking Skills exercise on p. 403

Write important vocabulary in the narrow column.

Write your notes in the wide column.

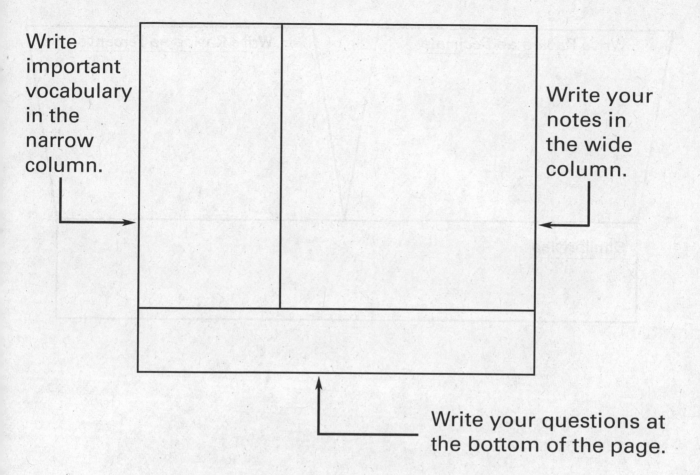

Write your questions at the bottom of the page.

Y Chart

For use with Notetaking Skills exercise on p. 414

Write Ratios as Decimals

Write Ratios as Percents

Similarities

Y Chart

For use with Notetaking Skills exercise on p. 424

Theoretical Probability

Experimental Probability

Similarities

Y Chart

For use with Notetaking Skills exercise on p. 450

Find Probability of Independent
Events

Find Probability of Dependent
Events

Similarities

Examples and Non-examples Chart

For use with Notetaking Skills exercise on p. 462

PROPORTIONS	
Examples	Non-Examples

Examples and Non-examples Chart

For use with Notetaking Skills exercise on p. 485

QUADRILATERALS	
Examples	Non-Examples

Examples and Non-examples Chart

For use with Notetaking Skills exercise on p. 503

CONGRUENT FIGURES	
Examples	Non-Examples

Information Wheel

For use with Notetaking Skills exercise on p. 514

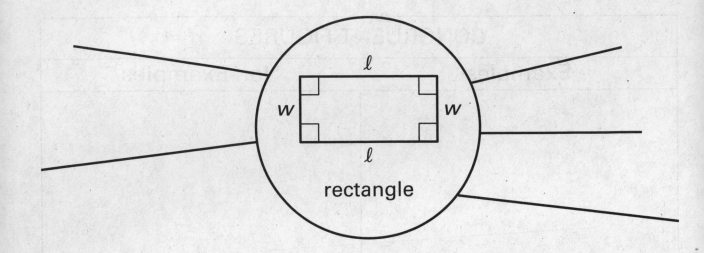

Information Wheel

For use with Notetaking Skills exercise on p. 536

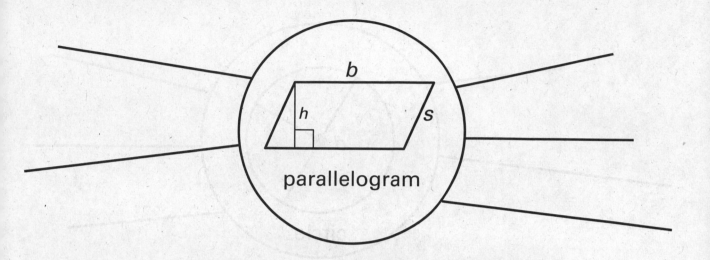

parallelogram

Information Wheel

For use with Notetaking Skills exercise on p. 563

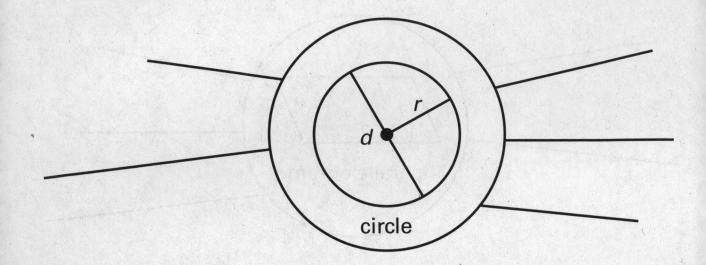

circle

Four Square Diagram

For use with Notetaking Skills exercise on p. 574

Definition:	Details:
Examples:	Non-Examples:

Four Square Diagram

For use with Notetaking Skills exercise on p. 577

Definition:	Details:
Examples:	Non-Examples:

Four Square Diagram

For use with Notetaking Skills exercise on p. 610

Definition:	Details:
Examples:	Non-Examples:

Definitions and Examples Chart

For use with Notetaking Skills exercise on p. 622

Formula:	Word and definition

	Example

	Example

	Example

Definitions and Examples Chart

For use with Notetaking Skills exercise on p. 632

Function:

Word and definition

Example

Example

Example

Definitions and Examples Chart

For use with Notetaking Skills exercise on p. 651

Slope:	Word and definition
	Example
	Example
	Example

Prime Factorization

Goal: Write a number as a product of prime numbers.

Vocabulary

Prime number:

Composite number:

Prime factorization:

Factor tree:

EXAMPLE 1 **Writing Factors of a Number**

Gardening Mrs. Gilbert bought 48 plants to put in her garden. She wants to break the plants up into groups that are the same size. Find the possible group sizes by writing all the factors of 48.

$48 = 1 \times \boxed{}$

$= 2 \times \boxed{}$

$= 3 \times \boxed{}$

$= 4 \times \boxed{}$ 48 isn't divisible by $\boxed{}$. Skip to $\boxed{}$.

$= 6 \times \boxed{}$ 48 isn't divisible by $\boxed{}$. Skip to $\boxed{}$.

$= 8 \times \boxed{}$ Stop when the factors $\boxed{}$.

Answer: The factors of 48 are $\boxed{}$.

EXAMPLE 2 **Identifying Prime and Composite Numbers**

Tell whether the number is *prime* or *composite*.

a. 52 **b.** 17

Solution

a. The factors of 52 are

[   ].

So, 52 is [   ].

b. The factors of 17 are

[   ]. So, 17 is [   ]

EXAMPLE 3 **Writing the Prime Factorization**

Use a factor tree to write the prime factorization of 36.

To *factor* a number means to write the number as a product of its factors.

One possible factor tree:

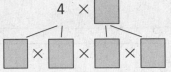

Write original number.

Factor 36 as 4 × [   ].

Factor 4 as [   ] × [   ] and [   ] as [   ] ×

Another possible factor tree:

Write original number.

Factor 36 as 3 × 12.

Factor 12 as 3 × [   ].

Factor [   ] as [   ] × [   ].

Both factor trees give the same result: 36 = [   ].

Answer: The prime factorization of 36 is [   ].

Guided Practice Use a factor tree to write the prime factorization of th[e] number.

1. 20	**2.** 32	**3.** 52	**4.** 68

Homework

Greatest Common Factor

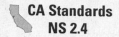

Goal: Find the greatest common factor of two or more numbers.

Vocabulary

Common factor:

Greatest common factor (GCF):

EXAMPLE 1 **Multiple Choice Practice**

The phrase "greatest common *divisor*" means the same as "greatest common *factor*."

What is the greatest common divisor of 18, 45, and 54?

  A 2   **B** 3   **C** 9   **D** 18

Solution

Write the divisors of 18, 45, and 54.

Divisors of 18:

Divisors of 45:

Divisors of 54:

The common divisors are [ ]. The greatest common divisor is [ ].

Answer: The correct answer is [ ]. **A** **B** **C** **D**

EXAMPLE 2 **Using the GCF to Solve Problems**

Flower Arranging A florist is making bouquets from 32 poppies, 40 irise[s] and 56 gerbera daisies. What is the greatest number of bouquets that th[e] florist can make using the same number of each flower in the bouquets? How many poppies, irises, and gerbera daisies will be in each bouquet?

Factors of 32: [_____]   The common factors are

Factors of 40: [_____]   [_____]. The G[CF]

Factors of 56: [_____] is [__].

Answer: The greatest common factor of 32, 40, and 56 is [__]. So, the

greatest number of bouquets that can be made is [__]. Then each bouq[uet]

will have [__] poppies, [__] irises, and [__] gerbera daisies.

Guided Practice Find the greatest common factor of the numbers by lis[ting] the factors.

1. 20, 35	**2.** 28, 49	**3.** 45, 60
4. 10, 24, 36	**5.** 15, 40, 50	**6.** 54, 72, 99

EXAMPLE **3**   **Using Prime Factorization to Find the GCF**

Find the greatest common factor of 120 and 165 using prime factorization.

Begin by writing the prime factorization of each number.

120

☐ × 12

☐ × ☐ × 2 × ☐

☐ × ☐ × 2 × ☐ × ☐

165

5 × ☐

☐ × ☐ × ☐

120: [_____]

165: [_____]

Answer: The common prime factors of 120 and 165 are ☐ and ☐.

So, the greatest common factor is ☐ × ☐ = ☐.

Large numbers may have many factors, and it may be difficult to list all the factors. It may be easier to use prime factorization to find the greatest common factor of large numbers.

Guided Practice   **Find the greatest common factor of the numbers using prime factorization.**

7. 100, 140	**8.** 96, 160
9. 108, 172	**10.** 200, 280

mework

Equivalent Fractions

Goal: Write equivalent fractions.

Vocabulary

Fraction:

Numerator:

Denominator:

Equivalent fractions:

Simplest form:

EXAMPLE 1 **Writing Fractions**

Radio There are 12 songs played in one hour on a local radio station. T
of the songs are new releases. What *fraction* of the songs played in an
are new releases?

The songs in the problem are arranged in the diagram. Using the diagra
you can write two equivalent fractions.

$$\frac{\text{Number of new releases}}{\text{Number of songs}} = \boxed{}$$

$$\frac{\text{Number of groups of 3 new releases}}{\text{Number of groups of 3 songs}} = \boxed{}$$

The fractions $\boxed{}$ and $\boxed{}$ are equivalent

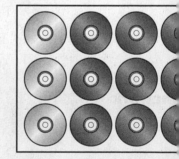

fractions because they represent the same
part-to-whole relationship.

EXAMPLE 2 **Writing Equivalent Fractions**

Write two fractions that are equivalent to $\frac{3}{9}$.

Multiply or divide the numerator and denominator by the same nonzero number to find an equivalent fraction.

$\frac{3}{9} = \dfrac{\boxed{} \times \boxed{}}{\boxed{} \times \boxed{}} = \frac{6}{18}$ Multiply numerator and denominator by $\boxed{}$.

$\frac{3}{9} = \dfrac{\boxed{} \div \boxed{}}{\boxed{} \div \boxed{}} = \frac{1}{3}$ Divide numerator and denominator by $\boxed{}$,

a common factor of $\boxed{}$ and $\boxed{}$.

EXAMPLE 3 **Simplifying Fractions**

Write the fraction in simplest form.

a. $\frac{10}{32}$ **b.** $\frac{9}{14}$

Solution

a $\frac{10}{32} = \dfrac{\boxed{} \times \boxed{}}{\boxed{} \times \boxed{}}$ The GCF of $\boxed{}$ and $\boxed{}$ is $\boxed{}$.

$= \boxed{}$

b. $\frac{9}{14}$ The GCF of $\boxed{}$ and $\boxed{}$ is $\boxed{}$.

The fraction is in simplest form.

Guided Practice **Write two fractions that are equivalent to the given fraction**

1. $\frac{1}{5}$	**2.** $\frac{7}{15}$	**3.** $\frac{10}{12}$	**4.** $\frac{20}{25}$

5. $\frac{12}{18}$	6. $\frac{20}{36}$	7. $\frac{15}{60}$	8. $\frac{24}{40}$

EXAMPLE 4 **Using Fractions in Simplest Form**

Student Council Janet and Bob are both running for Student Council Representative in their homerooms. Janet received 18 out of 30 votes in her homeroom. Bob received 15 out of 25 votes in his homeroom. Write the fraction of votes received by each candidate in simplest form. Are the fractions equivalent?

Janet

$$\frac{\text{Votes received}}{\text{Total votes in the homeroom}} = \frac{18}{30} = \boxed{} = \boxed{}$$

Bob

$$\frac{\text{Votes received}}{\text{Total votes in the homeroom}} = \frac{15}{25} = \boxed{} = \boxed{}$$

Answer: $\boxed{}$, $\frac{18}{30}$ and $\frac{15}{25}$ $\boxed{}$ equivalent fractions.

Homework

Word Triangle
For practicing notetaking skills

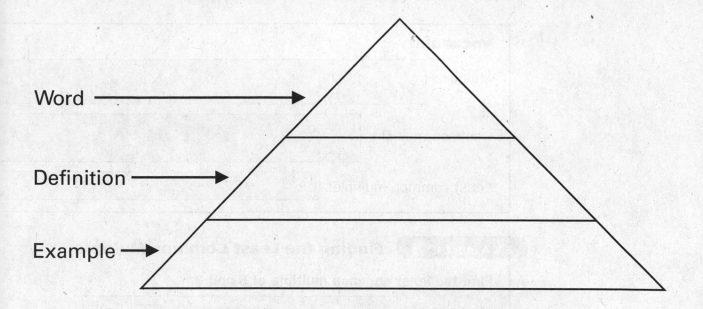

Word →

Definition →

Example →

Least Common Multiple

Goal: Find the LCM of two or more numbers.

Vocabulary

Multiple:

Common multiple:

Least common multiple:

EXAMPLE 1 **Finding the Least Common Multiple**

Find the least common multiple of 5 and 9.

Multiples of 5:

Multiples of 9:

Answer: The least common multiple of 5 and 9 is [ ].

Guided Practice Find the LCM of the numbers by listing the multiples.

1. 4, 7	**2.** 10, 15
3. 3, 8, 12	**4.** 2, 6, 10

EXAMPLE **2** **Using Prime Factorization to Find the LCM**

Find the LCM of 95 and 240 using prime factorization.

1. Begin by writing the prime factorization of each number.

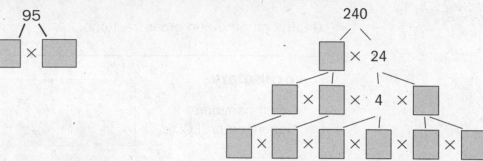

95: ▭

240: ▭

2. Circle the greatest power of every prime factor that appears in any of the prime factorizations.

95 = ▭   240 = ▭

3. Multiply the circled powers.

▭ = ▭

Answer: The least common multiple of 95 and 240 is ▭.

Guided Practice Find the LCM of the numbers using prime factorization.

5. 42, 70	**6.** 18, 27
7. 15, 20, 40	**8.** 45, 60, 72

e the prime
ization method
ind the least
mon multiple
rge numbers.

nework

LESSON 1.5

Comparing and Ordering Fractions

Goal: Compare and order fractions.

Vocabulary

Least common
denominator (LCD): [blank]

Comparing Two or More Fractions

1. Find the [blank] of the fractions.

2. Use the [blank] to write [blank] fractions.

3. Compare the [blank].

EXAMPLE 1 **Comparing Fractions Using the LCD**

Sewing Tara is sewing a red shirt and a blue shirt. The pattern for the shirt calls for $\frac{5}{8}$ yard of fabric. The pattern for the blue shirt calls for $\frac{7}{12}$ of fabric. Which shirt is made from more fabric?

Solution

1. Find the [blank] of the fractions.

Because the LCM of 8 and 12 is [blank], the [blank] is [blank].

2. Use the [blank] to write equivalent fractions.

Red: $\frac{5}{8} = \frac{}{} = \boxed{}$ **Blue:** $\frac{7}{12} = \frac{}{} = \boxed{}$

3. Compare the numerators: [blank], so $\frac{5}{8}$ [blank] $\frac{7}{12}$.

Answer: The [blank] shirt is made from more fabric.

EXAMPLE 2 **Multiple Choice Practice**

Which list shows $\frac{1}{4}$, $\frac{2}{5}$, $\frac{3}{10}$, and $\frac{5}{6}$ in order from least to greatest?

(A) $\frac{1}{4}$, $\frac{2}{5}$, $\frac{5}{6}$, $\frac{3}{10}$

(B) $\frac{5}{6}$, $\frac{1}{4}$, $\frac{2}{5}$, $\frac{3}{10}$

(C) $\frac{1}{4}$, $\frac{3}{10}$, $\frac{2}{5}$, $\frac{5}{6}$

(D) $\frac{3}{10}$, $\frac{5}{6}$, $\frac{2}{5}$, $\frac{1}{4}$

Solution

1. Find the LCD of the fractions.

   Because the LCM of 4, 5, 10, and 6 is ⬜ , the LCD is ⬜ .

2. Use the LCD to write equivalent fractions.

   $\frac{1}{4} = \dfrac{\boxed{}}{\boxed{}} = \boxed{}$ $\frac{2}{5} = \dfrac{\boxed{}}{\boxed{}} = \boxed{}$

   $\frac{3}{10} = \dfrac{\boxed{}}{\boxed{}} = \boxed{}$ $\frac{5}{6} = \dfrac{\boxed{}}{\boxed{}} = \boxed{}$

3. Compare the numerators: ⬜ , so ⬜

Answer: The order of the fractions from least to greatest, is

⬜ . The correct answer is ⬜ .   (A) (B) (C) (D)

Copy and complete the statement using <, >, or =.

1. $\frac{3}{5}$? $\frac{8}{13}$	2. $\frac{7}{8}$? $\frac{11}{12}$	3. $\frac{3}{7}$? $\frac{4}{11}$

Order the fractions from least to greatest.

4. $\frac{5}{6}$, $\frac{3}{4}$, $\frac{1}{2}$, $\frac{7}{12}$	5. $\frac{2}{9}$, $\frac{1}{6}$, $\frac{2}{3}$, $\frac{7}{18}$	6. $\frac{4}{5}$, $\frac{19}{20}$, $\frac{3}{4}$, $\frac{7}{10}$

EXAMPLE **3** **Comparing to One Half**

Which fraction is greater, $\frac{15}{32}$ or $\frac{23}{42}$?

Compare the numerator of each fraction to ▢ its denominator.

Decide if the fraction is greater than or less than ▢.

Because ▢ $< \frac{1}{2}$ ▢ you know that $\frac{15}{32}$ ▢ $\frac{1}{2}$.

Because ▢ $> \frac{1}{2}$ ▢ you know that $\frac{23}{42}$ ▢ $\frac{1}{2}$.

Answer: So, $\frac{15}{32}$ ▢ $\frac{23}{42}$.

Homework

Guided Practice Copy and complete the statement using $<$, $>$, or $=$.

7. $\frac{13}{28}$? $\frac{17}{32}$	**8.** $\frac{11}{20}$? $\frac{7}{16}$	**9.** $\frac{19}{36}$? $\frac{21}{44}$

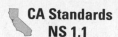
CA Standards
NS 1.1

Comparing Fractions and Mixed Numbers

Goal: Compare and order fractions and mixed numbers.

Vocabulary

Mixed number:

Proper fraction:

Improper fraction:

Writing Mixed Numbers as Improper Fractions

Words To write a mixed number as an improper fraction, multiply the

_____ and the _____ , add the

_____ , and write the sum _____ the denominator.

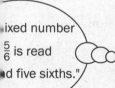

ixed number

$\frac{5}{6}$ is read

d five sixths."

Numbers $2\frac{5}{6} = $ _____ $= $ _____

EXAMPLE 1 **Writing Improper Fractions**

Write (a) $4\frac{2}{5}$ and (b) $3\frac{1}{9}$ as improper fractions.

a. $4\frac{2}{5} = $ _____ $= $ _____   **b.** $3\frac{1}{9} = $ _____ $= $ _____

Writing Improper Fractions as Mixed Numbers

Words To write an improper fraction as a mixed number, divide the [____] by the [____] and write any remainder as a [____].

Numbers $\dfrac{17}{5} \rightarrow 17 \div$ [____] $=$ [____] , or [____]

EXAMPLE 2 **Writing Mixed Numbers**

Need help with divisibility rules? See page 739 of your textbook.

Write $\dfrac{34}{5}$ as a mixed number.

1. Divide the numerator by the denominator.

2. Write the remainder R4 as a fraction: .

$$\dfrac{34}{5} = \boxed{} \div \boxed{} = \boxed{}$$

6 R4 $\rightarrow$ [____].

Answer: $\dfrac{34}{5} =$ [____]

Guided Practice Write the number as an improper fraction.

1. $2\dfrac{1}{3}$	**2.** 7	**3.** $3\dfrac{3}{4}$	**4.** $5\dfrac{2}{5}$

Write the improper fraction as a mixed number.

5. $\dfrac{17}{11}$	**6.** $\dfrac{19}{5}$	**7.** $\dfrac{22}{4}$	**8.** $\dfrac{27}{8}$

EXAMPLE **3** **Comparing Mixed Numbers and Fractions**

Compare $\frac{23}{8}$ and $2\frac{2}{3}$.

1. Write $2\frac{2}{3}$ as an improper fraction: $2\frac{2}{3} = \boxed{}$.

2. Rewrite $\frac{23}{8}$ and $\frac{8}{3}$ using the least common denominator of $\boxed{}$.

$$\frac{23}{8} = \frac{\boxed{}}{\boxed{}} = \boxed{} \qquad \frac{8}{3} = \frac{\boxed{}}{\boxed{}} = \boxed{}$$

3. Compare the fractions: $\boxed{}$, so $\frac{23}{8} \boxed{} 2\frac{2}{3}$.

EXAMPLE **4** **Ordering Mixed Numbers and Fractions**

County Fair The county fair holds a pie eating contest. Participants are to eat as many pies as they can in 10 minutes. Joe ate $4\frac{1}{4}$ pies, Conan ate 5 pies, David ate $\frac{22}{5}$ pies, and Jonathan ate $4\frac{1}{2}$ pies. Order the amounts of pie the contestants ate from least to greatest.

Solution

The denominators are 4, 1 $\left(\text{because } 5 = \boxed{}\right)$, 5, and 2. Write the numbers as improper fractions using the least common denominator of $\boxed{}$.

$$4\frac{1}{4} = \boxed{} = \frac{\boxed{}}{\boxed{}} = \boxed{} \qquad 5 = \boxed{} = \frac{\boxed{}}{\boxed{}} = \boxed{}$$

$$\frac{22}{5} = \frac{\boxed{}}{\boxed{}} = \boxed{} \qquad 4\frac{1}{2} = \boxed{} = \frac{\boxed{}}{\boxed{}} = \boxed{}$$

Answer: From least to greatest, the amounts of pie the contestants ate are $\boxed{}$.

 nework

Word Triangle

For use with homework

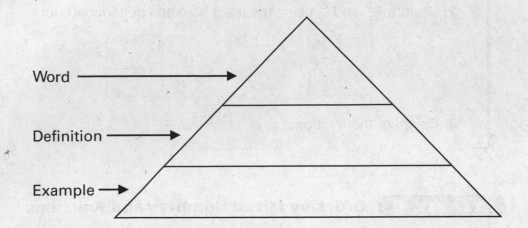

Word ➞

Definition ➞

Example ➞

Ordering Fractions and Decimals

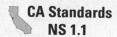

Goal: Write fractions as decimals and decimals as fractions.

Vocabulary

Terminating decimal:

Repeating decimal:

EXAMPLE 1 **Writing Fractions as Decimals**

Write (a) $\frac{5}{8}$ and (b) $2\frac{3}{5}$ as decimals.

Solution

a.

$8\overline{)5.000}$ ← Write zeros in dividend as placeholders.

← Remainder is [ ].

Answer: $\frac{5}{8} = $ [ ]

b.

$5\overline{)3.0}$ ← Write a zero in dividend as a placeholder.

← Remainder is [ ].

Answer: $2\frac{3}{5} = $ [ ] $+$ [ ] $= $ [ ]

Write the fraction or mixed number as a decimal.

1. $\frac{7}{10}$	2. $\frac{25}{400}$	3. $4\frac{3}{4}$	4. $3\frac{1}{8}$

EXAMPLE 2 Writing Fractions as Repeating Decimals

Write (a) $\frac{11}{6}$ and (b) $\frac{14}{15}$ as decimals.

Solution

a.
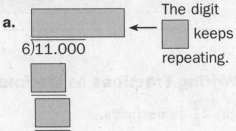
The digit ___ keeps repeating.

$6\overline{)11.000}$

Remainder will never be ___ .

Answer: $\frac{11}{6} = $ ___

b.
15$\overline{)14.000}$

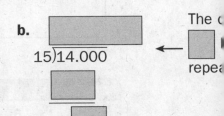
The d___

repea___

Remainder never be ___

Answer: $\frac{14}{15} = $ ___

EXAMPLE 3 Writing Decimals as Fractions

Write (a) 0.72 and (b) 3.875 as a fraction or mixed number.

Solution

a. $0.72 = \dfrac{72}{\boxed{}}$

2 is in the ___ place.

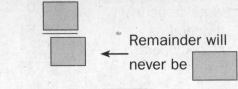

$= \dfrac{\boxed{} \times \frac{1}{4}}{\boxed{} \times \frac{4}{1}}$

$= \boxed{}$

b. $3.875 = 3\dfrac{875}{\boxed{}}$

5 is in the ___ place.

$= 3\dfrac{\boxed{} \times \frac{1}{125}}{\boxed{} \times \frac{125}{1}}$

$= \boxed{}$

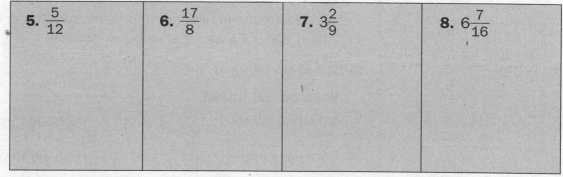

EXAMPLE 4 **Ordering Numbers**

Veterinarian Jorja's cat gave birth to a litter of kittens. She took the kittens to the veterinarian for a check-up. The kittens' weights were recorded for their medical records. What is the order of the kittens from least to greatest weight?

Kitten 1: $\frac{5}{6}$ pound = ☐ pound

Kitten 2: $\frac{2}{5}$ pound = ☐ pound

Kitten 3: $\frac{1}{4}$ pound = ☐ pound

Kitten 4: $\frac{3}{8}$ pound = ☐ pound

Answer: Because ☐ < ☐ < ☐ < ☐, the kittens are, from least to greatest weight, Kitten ☐, Kitten ☐, Kitten ☐, and Kitten ☐.

nly the
) under the
should be
In Example 4,
1's weight
as a decimal
= 0.8333...,
838383....

Guided Practice Write the fraction or mixed number as a decimal.

5. $\frac{5}{12}$	**6.** $\frac{17}{8}$	**7.** $3\frac{2}{9}$	**8.** $6\frac{7}{16}$

Write the decimal as a fraction or mixed number.

9. 0.8	**10.** 3.35	**11.** 0.625	**12.** 1.175

mework

A Problem Solving Plan

CA Standa
MR 1.
MR 2.
MR 3.

Goal: Use a 4-step plan to solve many kinds of problems.

EXAMPLE 1 **Understanding and Planning**

Football The table shows the number of passes thrown and complete
by two players on a football team. With Cory's next few passes thrown
hopes to have a greater fraction of passes completed than Mike. How
completed passes in a row does Cory need to do this?

Name	Passes thrown	Passes completed
Mike	16	4
Cory	25	4

To solve this problem, you need to make sure you understand the pro
lem. Then make a plan for solving the problem.

Read and Understand
What do you Know?

Mike has completed ☐ out of ☐ passes thrown.

Cory has completed ☐ out of ☐ passes thrown.

Make a Plan
How can you relate what you know to what you want to find ou

Need help
with problem
solving strategies?
See pages 690-691
of your textbook.

1. In the table, what is Mike's fraction of passes completed?

2. What is Cory's fraction of passes completed?

EXAMPLE 2 Solving and Looking Back

To solve the problem from the previous page, carry out the plan from Example 1 and then check the answer.

Solve the Problem

Mike has completed $\frac{4}{16} = \boxed{}$ of his passes. Cory has completed $\frac{4}{25} = \boxed{}$, of his passes. Increase Cory's passes thrown and completed by 1. Then find the fraction of his passes completed. Record your results in a table. Keep increasing the passes until his fraction is greater than $\boxed{}$.

Passes Completed in a Row	Total Passes Completed	Total Passes Thrown	Fraction of Passes Completed
1	5	26	$\boxed{} \approx \boxed{}$
2	6	27	$\boxed{} \approx \boxed{}$
3	7	28	$\boxed{} \approx \boxed{}$
4	8	29	$\boxed{} \approx \boxed{}$

Answer: Cory needs to complete $\boxed{}$ passes in a row to have a greater fraction of passes completed than Mike.

Look Back

After Cory makes $\boxed{}$ completed passes in a row, he has the $\boxed{}$ fraction of passes completed as Mike. So, it is reasonable that if he completes his next pass, he will have a $\boxed{}$ fraction of passes completed than Mike.

Need help place value? e page 676 ur textbook.

3. Suppose Cory does not complete his first pass and now has completed 4 of his 26 passes. How many passes does he need to complete in a row to exceed Mike's fraction of passes completed?

A Problem Solving Plan

1. _____

Distinguish between _____ and _____. Ider

_____. _____ and _____ information.

2. _____

Identify _____. Observe _____. Determine whether problem can be broken into _____. Make _____. Determine whether the answer needs to be _____ or can be

_____.

3. _____

Apply _____ from _____ problems. _____ conjectures. Use _____, then make _____ and give the answer to an _____. Express the _____ clearly; explain _____.

4. _____

Check the _____ of the solution using _____ and the _____. Generalize _____.

Word Triangle

For use with homework

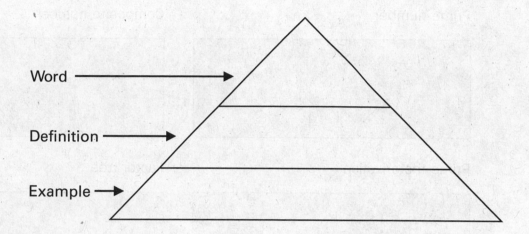

Word →

Definition →

Example →

Words to Review

Give an example of the vocabulary word.

Prime number

Composite number

Prime factorization

Factor tree

Common factor

Greatest common factor

Fraction

Numerator

Denominator

Equivalent fractions

Simplest from

Multiples

Common multiples

Least common multiple

Least common denominator

Mixed number

Proper fraction

Improper fraction

Terminating decimal

Repeating decimal

Review your notes and Chapter 1 by using the Chapter Review on pages 56–60 of your textbook.

Adding and Subtracting Fractions

CA Stand
NS 2.

Goal: Add and subtract fractions.

Vocabulary

Variable:

Algebraic expression:

Evaluate:

Fractions with Common Denominators

Words To add or subtract two fractions with a common denominator, w

the ___ or ___ of the numerators over the ___

Numbers $\frac{1}{5} + \frac{2}{5} = $ ___ **Algebra** $\frac{a}{c} + \frac{b}{c} = $ ___ $(c \neq 0$

$\frac{4}{7} - \frac{1}{7} = $ ___ $\frac{a}{c} - \frac{b}{c} = $ ___ $(c \neq 0$

EXAMPLE 1 **Adding and Subtracting Fractions**

a. $\frac{2}{7} + \frac{3}{7} = $ ___ Add numerators.

$= $ ___ Simplify numerator.

b. $\frac{4}{9} - \frac{1}{9} = $ ___ Subtract numerators.

$= $ ___ Simplify numerator.

$= $ ___ Simplify fraction.

> Need help with simplifying fractions? See page 17 of your textbook.

1. $\frac{3}{10} + \frac{1}{10}$	2. $\frac{2}{11} + \frac{8}{11}$	3. $\frac{6}{7} - \frac{4}{7}$	4. $\frac{8}{15} - \frac{3}{15}$

EXAMPLE 2 **Evaluating Variable Expressions**

Evaluate the expression $x - \frac{1}{8}$ for (a) $x = \frac{2}{8}$ and (b) $x = \frac{3}{8}$.

> After making e substitutions in Example 2, he results are erical expressions. To simplify a erical expression, perform all the operations

a. $x - \frac{1}{8} = $ ☐   Substitute ☐ for x.

      $= $ ☐   Subtract.

b. $x - \frac{1}{8} = $ ☐   Substitute ☐ for x.

      $= $ ☐   Subtract.

      $= $ ☐   Simplify.

Guided Practice Evaluate the expression when $c = \frac{6}{11}$.

iework

5. $\frac{2}{11} + c$	6. $c - \frac{5}{11}$

Using a Common Denominator

CA Stand
NS 2.

Goal: Add and subtract fractions with different denominators.

Adding or Subtracting Fractions with Different Denominato

1. Rewrite the fractions using the ☐ .

2. Add or subtract the ☐ .

3. Write the result over the ☐ .

4. ☐ if possible.

EXAMPLE 1 **Multiple Choice Practice**

What is the value of $\frac{1}{4} + \frac{3}{5}$?

(A) $\frac{1}{5}$ (B) $\frac{1}{4}$ (C) $\frac{4}{5}$ (D) $\frac{17}{20}$

Solution

$$\frac{\square \times \square}{\square \times \square} = \square \qquad \text{Rewrite both fractions using the LCD, } \square.$$

$$+ \frac{\square \times \square}{\square \times \square} = + \square$$

$$\square \qquad \text{Add the fractions}$$

Answer: The correct answer is ☐ . (A) (B) (C) (D)

EXAMPLE 2 **Rewriting Sums of Fractions**

$\dfrac{3}{4} + \dfrac{4}{5} =$ [ ]   Find equivalent fractions using the LCD, 20.

$=$ [ ]   Rewrite.

$=$ [ ] , or [ ]   Add the fractions. Rewrite as a mixed number.

Need help with writing improper fractions as mixed numbers? See page 35 of your textbook.

✓ **Check**   You can use estimation to check that your answer is reasonable. Because $\dfrac{3}{4}$ is [ ] $\dfrac{1}{2}$ and $\dfrac{4}{5}$ is [ ] $\dfrac{1}{2}$, the sum of $\dfrac{3}{4}$ and $\dfrac{4}{5}$ should be [ ] than 1.

EXAMPLE 3 **Subtracting Fractions**

Find the difference $\dfrac{5}{6} - \dfrac{2}{9}$.

Solution

$\dfrac{5}{6} - \dfrac{2}{9} =$ [ ]   Find equivalent fractions using the LCD, [ ].

$=$ [ ]   Rewrite.

$=$ [ ]   Subtract the fractions.

EXAMPLE **4** **Rewriting 1 as a Fraction**

Travel The usual flight from Houston to Dallas takes 1 hour. Due to favorable weather conditions, today's flight only takes $\frac{3}{4}$ hour. How much faster was today's flight than usual?

Solution

To find out how much faster the flight was, you need to find the

[   ] of 1 and [   ]. You can rewrite 1 as [   ].

$1 - \frac{3}{4} = $ [   ] $-$ [   ]   Rewrite 1 as [   ]

$= $ [   ]   Subtract the fractions.

Answer: Today's flight was [   ] hour faster.

Guided Practice Add or subtract. Simplify if possible.

1. $\frac{1}{3} + \frac{4}{15}$	**2.** $\frac{5}{8} + \frac{11}{12}$	**3.** $\frac{5}{6} - \frac{2}{3}$	**4.** $\frac{7}{10} - \frac{1}{4}$
5. $\frac{6}{7} + \frac{1}{2}$	**6.** $\frac{5}{12} + \frac{1}{9}$	**7.** $1 - \frac{3}{8}$	**8.** $1 - \frac{2}{13}$

Homework

CA Standards
NS 2.1

Adding and Subtracting Mixed Numbers

Goal: Add and subtract mixed numbers.

Adding and Subtracting Mixed Numbers

1. Find the ▢ of the fractions, if necessary.

2. ▢ the fractions, if necessary. Then add or subtract the fractions.

3. Add or subtract the ▢.

4. ▢ if possible.

EXAMPLE 1 **Adding with a Common Denominator**

Garden Javier bought $23\frac{1}{5}$ pounds of humus to build a vegetable garden. He topped the garden with $25\frac{2}{5}$ pounds of mulch. How much garden material did he put in the vegetable garden?

To solve the problem, you need to find the sum of $23\frac{1}{5}$ and $25\frac{2}{5}$.

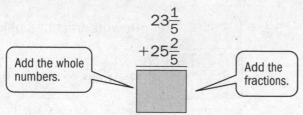

$$23\frac{1}{5}$$
$$+25\frac{2}{5}$$

Add the whole numbers.

Add the fractions.

Answer: Javier put ▢ lb of garden material in the vegetable garden.

EXAMPLE 2 **Subtracting with a Common Denominator**

$4\frac{5}{8} - 2\frac{1}{8} = $ ▢   Subtract fractions and whole numbers.

$= $ ▢   Simplify.

Add or subtract. Simplify if possible.

1. $5\frac{3}{10} + 2\frac{1}{10}$	**2.** $6\frac{1}{6} + 1\frac{2}{6}$	**3.** $7\frac{4}{9} - 3\frac{1}{9}$	**4.** $15\frac{7}{8} - 7\frac{7}{8}$

EXAMPLE 3 Adding with Different Denominators

In Example 3, you can estimate the answer by rounding each mixed number to the nearest whole number. By doing so, you have 4 + 6 = 10, so your answer is reasonable.

$3\frac{1}{2} + 5\frac{3}{4} = \boxed{}$ Rewrite fractions using the LCD of $\boxed{}$ and $\boxed{}$

$= \boxed{}$ Add fractions and whole numbers.

$= \boxed{}$ Write 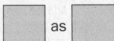 as a mixed num

$= \boxed{}$ Add whole numbers.

EXAMPLE 4 Renaming to Subtract Mixed Numbers

$8\frac{1}{10} - 5\frac{3}{5} = \boxed{}$ Rewrite fractions using the LCD of $\boxed{}$ and

$= \boxed{}$ Rename $\boxed{}$ as $\boxed{}$.

$= \boxed{}$ Subtract fractions and whole numbers.

$= \boxed{}$ Simplify.

Add or subtract. Simplify if possible.

Homework

5. $3\frac{1}{6} + 1\frac{2}{3}$	**6.** $7\frac{1}{2} + 2\frac{2}{3}$	**7.** $10 - 3\frac{2}{5}$	**8.** $7\frac{1}{5} - 6\frac{5}{6}$

Concept Map

For practicing notetaking skills

Multiplying Fractions and Mixed Numbers

Goal: Multiply fractions and mixed numbers.

> A multiplication dot as in • is sometimes used in place of an ✕ to avoid confusion with the variable X.

Multiplying Fractions

Words The product of two or more fractions is equal to the product of the [   ] over the product of the [   ].

Numbers $\dfrac{2}{9} \bullet \dfrac{4}{5} = $ [   ]   **Algebra** $\dfrac{a}{b} \bullet \dfrac{c}{d} = $ [   ] $(b, d \neq 0)$

EXAMPLE 1 **Multiplying Fractions**

Baking Eva's bread recipe calls for $\dfrac{1}{4}$ cup of olive oil. She only wants to make half of the recipe. How much olive oil does Eva need?

$\dfrac{1}{2} \times \dfrac{1}{4} = $ [   ]   Use rule for multiplying fractions.

= [   ]   Multiply.

Answer: Eva needs [   ] cup of olive oil for half of the bread recipe.

✓ **Check:** Use a model to find the product.

Guided Practice Find the product. Simplify if possible.

1. $\dfrac{3}{4} \times \dfrac{1}{2}$	**2.** $\dfrac{7}{10} \times \dfrac{1}{3}$	**3.** $\dfrac{2}{5} \times \dfrac{5}{8}$	**4.** $\dfrac{2}{3} \times \dfrac{3}{4}$

Copyright © by McDougal Littell, a division of Houghton Mifflin

EXAMPLE 2 Multiplying Whole Numbers and Fractions

Bus At Jefferson Middle School, $\frac{2}{5}$ of the students ride the bus to and from school. If 750 students attend Jefferson Middle School, how many students take the bus to and from school?

Solution

$\frac{2}{5} \times 750 =$ [   ] Write 750 as $\frac{750}{1}$.

$=$ [   ] Use rule for multiplying fractions. Divide out the GCF of [   ] and [   ].

$=$ [   ], or [   ] Multiply.

Answer: There are [   ] students who take the bus to and from school.

EXAMPLE 3 Multiplying Mixed Numbers

$2\frac{4}{5} \times 2\frac{1}{12} =$ [   ] Write [   ] and [   ] as improper fractions.

$=$ [   ] Use rule for multiplying fractions. Divide out GCF of [   ] and [   ] and GCF of [   ] and [   ].

$=$ [   ] Multiply.

$=$ [   ] Write as a mixed number.

Guided Practice Find the product. Simplify if possible.

nework

5. $6 \times \frac{1}{4}$	**6.** $\frac{2}{3} \times 10$	**7.** $3\frac{9}{10} \times 2\frac{2}{3}$	**8.** $2\frac{1}{2} \times 7\frac{4}{15}$

Dividing Fractions and Mixed Numbers

Goal: Divide fractions and mixed numbers.

Vocabulary

Reciprocal:

Using Reciprocals to Divide

Words To divide by any nonzero number, multiply by its _____.

Numbers $\dfrac{3}{4} \div \dfrac{2}{3} =$ _____ =

Algebra $\dfrac{a}{b} \div \dfrac{c}{d} =$ _____ = _____ $(b, c, d \neq 0)$

EXAMPLE 1 **Dividing a Fraction by a Fraction**

$\dfrac{3}{5} \div \dfrac{9}{10} =$

Multiply by reciprocal.

$=$

Use rule for multiplying fractions.
Divide out common factors.

$=$

Multiply.

EXAMPLE 2 **Dividing a Fraction by a Whole Number**

$\dfrac{3}{8} \div 6 =$

Multiply by reciprocal.

$=$

Use rule for multiplying fractions.
Divide out common factor.

$=$

Multiply.

In Example 2, you can check your answer by multiplying the quotient and the divisor and comparing the result with the dividend:
$\dfrac{1}{16} \times 6 = \dfrac{1}{16} \times \dfrac{6}{1} = \dfrac{3}{8}.$

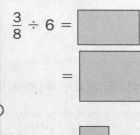

Find the quotient. Simplify if possible.

1. $\frac{5}{12} \div \frac{1}{10}$	**2.** $\frac{8}{3} \div \frac{4}{9}$	**3.** $\frac{3}{4} \div 9$	**4.** $\frac{2}{5} \div 8$

EXAMPLE 3 Drawing a Diagram to Solve a Problem

Craft Fair Organizers of a craft show have to place a cone on the sidewalk every $2\frac{1}{2}$ yards to mark where the craft vendors can set up their booths. One sidewalk that will be used in the craft show is 20 yards long. How many cones must be placed along this sidewalk?

Solution

Method 1 Draw a diagram on graph paper. Make the sidewalk 20 grid boxes long.

Draw a point to mark the location of a cone every $2\frac{1}{2}$ grid boxes but not at the start or end.

Method 2 Use division.

$20 \div 2\frac{1}{2} = \boxed{}$ Write $\boxed{}$ as an improper fraction.

$= \boxed{}$ Multiply by reciprocal.

$= \boxed{}$ Use rule for multiplying fractions.
Divide out common factor.

$= \boxed{}$ Multiply.

The quotient $\boxed{}$ gives you the number of *spaces*, not the number of *cones*. Subtract $\boxed{}$ to get the number of cones.

$\boxed{} = \boxed{}$

Answer: $\boxed{}$ cones must be placed along this sidewalk.

EXAMPLE 4 **Multiple Choice Practice**

What is the value of $7\frac{1}{3} \div 1\frac{8}{9}$?

A $\frac{17}{66}$ **B** $3\frac{15}{17}$ **C** $8\frac{1}{4}$ **D** $13\frac{23}{27}$

$7\frac{1}{3} \div 1\frac{8}{9} = $    Write ☐ and ☐ as improper fract▮

$= $ ☐   Multiply by reciprocal.

$= $ ☐   Use rule for multiplying fractions.
Divide out common factor.

$= $ ☐ , or ☐   Multiply.

Answer: The correct answer is .   **A** **B** **C** **D**

Guided Practice Find the quotient. Then check the answer.

Homework	**5.** $5 \div \frac{10}{11}$	**6.** $8 \div 4\frac{4}{5}$	**7.** $3\frac{3}{5} \div \frac{1}{4}$	**8.** $1\frac{1}{6} \div 1\frac{1}{3}$

Concept Map

For use with homework

Adding and Subtracting Decimals

LESSON 2.6

Goal: Add and subtract decimals.

Vocabulary

Front-end estimation:

EXAMPLE 1 **Adding and Subtracting Decimals**

a. 2.149 + 1.32

$$
\begin{array}{r}
2.149 \\
+\ 1.320 \\
\hline
\end{array}
$$
← Write ☐ as a placeholder.

b. 5 − 3.18

$$
\begin{array}{r}
5.00 \\
-\ 3.18 \\
\hline
\end{array}
$$
← Write ☐ as placeholders.

Guided Practice **Find the sum or difference.**

1. 42.9 + 26.5	**2.** 4.62 + 3.4	**3.** 2.859 + 3.48
4. 2.5 − 0.9	**5.** 8.43 − 6.21	**6.** 1 − 0.16

EXAMPLE 2 Evaluating an Expression

Evaluate 4.9 + t + 3.8 when t = 3.42.

Solution

$$4.9 + t + 3.8 = 4.9 + \boxed{} + 3.8 \qquad \text{Substitute } \boxed{} \text{ for } t.$$

$$= \boxed{} + 3.8 \qquad \boxed{}$$

$$= \boxed{} \qquad \boxed{}$$

Guided Practice Evaluate the expression when *d* = 5.82 and *t* = 4.9.

7. *d* + 6.6	**8.** 13.51 − *t*	**9.** *d* − 1.7

EXAMPLE 3 Estimating a Sum

Lunch Joel and Manny are eating lunch at a deli. Joel's lunch costs
$6.75, and Manny's lunch costs $5.40. They want to order two
chocolate shakes, which will cost an additional $3.89. They have
$15.00 to pay the bill. Can they buy the milkshakes?

Solution

1. Add the front-end
digits: the dollars.

$**6**.75

$**5**.40

+ $**3**.89
_____

$\boxed{}$

2. Estimate the sum
of the remaining
digits: the cents.

$6.**75** ↘

$5.**40** → $\boxed{}$

+ $3.**89** ↗ $\boxed{}$

$\boxed{}$

3. Add the results.

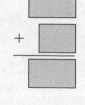

Answer: The estimated sum is $\boxed{}$ than $15, so they $\boxed{}$ buy
the milkshakes.

Multiplying and Dividing Decimals

Goal: Multiply and divide decimals.

Vocabulary

Leading digit:

Compatible Numbers:

Multiplying Decimals

Words Multiply decimals as you would [   ]. Then place

the [   ] in the product. The number of decimal places in t

product is equal to [   ]

[   ].

Numbers $0.7 \times 0.3 =$ [   ]

EXAMPLE 1 **Multiplying Decimals**

```
    2.56          [    ] decimal places

  × 0.43        + [    ] decimal places
    768
  1024
  1.1008          [    ] decimal places
```

EXAMPLE **2** **Multiplying Decimals**

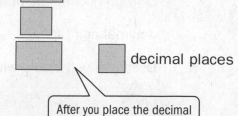

a. 0.55 ⬚ decimal places

⬚⬚⬚ × 12 + ⬚ decimal places

⬚ decimal places

> After you place the decimal point, you can ⬚ any zeros at the end of an answer.

Answer: 0.55 × 12 = ⬚

✓ **Check** Because $\frac{1}{2}$ of 12 is ⬚ , the product is reasonable.

b. 1.168 ⬚ decimal places

× 0.07 + ⬚ decimal places

⬚ decimal places

> Write a ⬚ before the 8 as a placeholder so that the number has five decimal places.

Answer: 1.168 × 0.07 = ⬚

✓ **Check** Because 1 × 0.07 = ⬚ , the product is reasonable.

Find the product. Then check that your answer is reasonable.

1. 2.5 × 3.9	**2.** 0.43 × 0.16	**3.** 5.103 × 2.9

EXAMPLE 3 **Dividing a Decimal by a Whole Number**

Gift Joy and her three cousins spent $21.40 on a gift for their grandfath
Each cousin contributed the same amount of money. How much did each
cousin spend?

[ ])21.40

Line up decimal point in [   ] with

decimal point in [   ].

Divide as you would with [   ]

Answer: Each cousin spent [   ]

Guided Practice **Find the quotient.**

4. 253.4 ÷ 7	5. 14.76 ÷ 3	6. 91.8 ÷ 9

Dividing by a Decimal

Words When you divide by a decimal, multiply both the divisor and

the dividend by a [   ] that will make the divisor a

[   ].

Numbers   12.5)8.75 ⟶ [   ])87.5 ← 0.7

EXAMPLE 4 **Dividing Decimals**

a. $0.002\overline{)6.826}$ To multiply divisor and dividend by ☐,

move both decimal points ☐ place(s) to the right.

$$
\begin{array}{r}
3413 \\
2\overline{)6826} \\
\underline{6} \\
8 \\
\underline{8} \\
2 \\
\underline{2} \\
6 \\
\underline{6} \\
0
\end{array}
$$

b. $2.4\overline{)12.0}$ To multiply divisor and dividend by ☐, move both decimal points ☐ place(s) to the right. Write ☐ as a placeholder.

$$
\begin{array}{r}
5 \\
24\overline{)120} \\
\underline{120} \\
0
\end{array}
$$

c. $0.5\overline{)0.028}$ To multiply divisor and dividend by 10, move both decimal points ☐ place(s) to the right.

$$
\begin{array}{r}
0.056 \\
5\overline{)0.28} \\
\underline{25} \\
30 \\
\underline{30} \\
0
\end{array}
$$

Line up ☐.

TCH OUT!
forget to write
as placeholders
quotient.

Guided Practice **Find the quotient. Round to the nearest hundredth if necessary.**

7. $19.6 \div 0.5$	**8.** $48.45 \div 5.7$	**9.** $0.495 \div 8.25$
10. $16.0125 \div 9.15$	**11.** $75 \div 3.2$	**12.** $9.6 \div 4$

Concept Map

For use with homework

Words to Review

Give an example of the vocabulary word.

Variable

Algebraic Expression

Evaluate

Reciprocal

Front-end estimation

Leading digit

Compatible numbers

Review your notes and Chapter 2 by using the Chapter Review on pages 117–120 of your textbook.

Ordering Integers on a Number Line

Goal: Order integers using a number line.

Vocabulary

Integer:

Negative integer:

Positive integer:

Opposite:

Integers and Their Opposites

> The integer −3 is read "negative three." A number other than 0 that has no sign is considered to be positive, so the integer 3 is read "positive three" or "three."

Zero

Negative integers   Positive integers

−4 −3 −2 −1 0 1 2 3 4

Two numbers are **opposites** if they are the [_____] from zero

a number line but are on [_____] of zero. For example, −3

the opposite of [__]. The opposite of 0 is [__].

EXAMPLE 1 **Writing Integers**

Temperatures The temperature increased 12 degrees between 7 A.M. and 7 P.M. The temperature decreased 14 degrees between 7 P.M. and 7 A.M. Use integers to represent the increase and decrease in the temperature.

Solution

12 degree increase: [____]   14 degree decrease: [____]

Write the opposite of the integer.

1. −17	**2.** 3	**3.** 41	**4.** −215

EXAMPLE 2 **Comparing Integers Using a Number Line**

a. Compare −1 and −4.

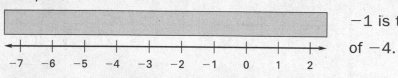

−1 is to the ☐ of −4.

Answer: −1 ☐ −4, or −4 ☐ −1.

b. Compare −3 and 0.

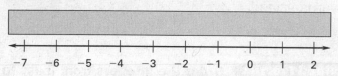

−3 is to the ☐ of 0.

Answer: −3 ☐ 0, or 0 ☐ −3.

(left margin)
'CH OUT!
confuse a
ve sign with a
ction sign. A
ve sign indicates
ction on a number
t an operation.

Guided Practice Copy and complete the statement using < or >.

5. 3 __?__ −5	**6.** −7 __?__ 2	**7.** −6 __?__ −8	**8.** −2 __?__ −10

EXAMPLE 3   **Ordering Integers Using a Number Line**

Football The table shows the number of yards gained by the West High School football team during the first play in each quarter during their first game of the season. Which quarter had the first play with the least yards gained?

Quarter	1	2	3	4	OT
Yards Gained During First Play	15	−7	−12	9	19

Solution

You can graph each integer on a number line to order the yards gained.

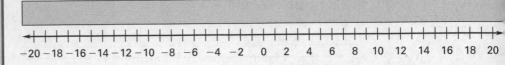

−20 −18 −16 −14 −12 −10 −8 −6 −4 −2 0 2 4 6 8 10 12 14 16 18 20

The yardages from least to greatest are: .

Answer: At   yards, the first play of the   quarter had the

yards gained.

Guided Practice   **Order the integers from least to greatest.**

Homework

9. −4, −9, −1, −7, 0

10. 6, −2, 3, −5, −10

Adding Integers

Goal: Add integers.

Vocabulary

Absolute value:

EXAMPLE 1 **Using a Number Line to Add Integers**

Find the sum $-4 + (-2)$ using a number line.

Start at 0. Move [ ] units to the [ ].

Then move [ ] more units to the [ ].

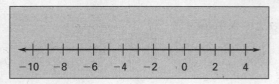

Answer: The final position is [ ], so $-4 + (-2) = $ [ ].

EXAMPLE 2 **Multiple Choice Practice**

The number line shows changes in altitude of a glider. Which expression represents the new altitude of the glider?

Ⓐ $-14 + 8$ Ⓑ $14 + 0$ Ⓒ $14 + (-8)$ Ⓓ $14 + (-6)$

Solution

The model represents moving [ ] units to the right and then [ ] units to the left, or [ ] + [ ] = [ ].

Answer: The correct answer is [ ].   Ⓐ Ⓑ Ⓒ Ⓓ

Guided Practice Use a number line to find the sum.

1. $-7 + (-2)$	**2.** $-9 + 5$	**3.** $7 + (-12)$	**4.** $18 + (-5)$

EXAMPLE 3 **Finding Absolute Value**

Find the absolute value of the number.

a. 4

b. -5

Solution

a. The distance between 4 and 0 is ☐. So, $|4| =$ ☐.

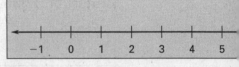

b. The distance between -5 and 0 is ☐. So, $|-5| =$ ☐.

Because distance cannot be negative, the absolute value of a number cannot be negative.

Guided Practice Find the absolute value of the number.

5. 75	**6.** -10	**7.** -60	**8.** 36

Adding Integers with Absolute Value

Words

Same Sign Add the [____] and use the [____] sign.

Different Signs Subtract the [____] from the [____] and use the sign of the integer with the [____].

Opposites The sum of an integer and its [____] is [____].

Numbers

$10 + 14 =$ [____]

$-7 + (-5) =$ [____]

$13 + (-9) =$ [____]

$-11 + 6 =$ [____]

$-4 + 4 =$ [____]

EXAMPLE 4 **Adding Two Integers Using Absolute Value**

a. Find the sum $-2 + (-11)$.

These integers have [____].

Add $|$[____]$|$ and $|$[____]$|$.

$-2 + (-11) =$ [____]

Both integers are [____], so the sum is [____].

b. Find the sum $-4 + 7$.

These integers have [____].

Subtract $|$[____]$|$ from $|$[____]$|$.

$-4 + 7 =$ [____]

Because $|$[____]$| \; |$[____]$| \; |$[____]$|$, the sum has the same sign as [____].

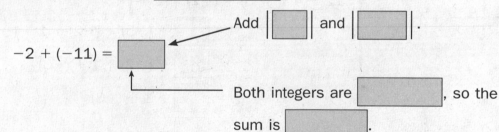

9. $-3 + (-9)$	**10.** $-8 + 4$	**11.** $0 + (-13)$
12. $-10 + 12$	**13.** $18 + (-10)$	**14.** $-25 + 25$

EXAMPLE 5 **Adding Three or More Integers**

Stock Market The stock price of the Morello Corporation changed every day this week. Find the value of the stock at the end of the week.

Starting Price: $1
Monday $
Tuesday $-$
Wednesday $-$
Thursday $
Friday $-$

Solution

You can find the sum by adding the integers two at a time.

$12 + 4 + (-5) + (-2) + 1 + (-3)$

$\quad = \boxed{} + (-5) + (-2) + 1 + (-3)$ ⟶ Add 12 and 4.

$\quad = \boxed{} + (-2) + 1 + (-3)$ ⟶ Add $\boxed{}$ and

$\quad = \boxed{} + 1 + (-3)$ ⟶ Add $\boxed{}$ and

$\quad = \boxed{} + (-3)$ ⟶ Add $\boxed{}$ and

$\quad = \boxed{}$ ⟶ Add $\boxed{}$ and

Answer: The sum of the starting price and the changes in the stock pri is $\boxed{}$. The stock was valued at $\$\boxed{}$ at the end of the week.

Guided Practice **Refer to Example 5.**

Homework

15. During the next week, the stock changed value again.

$\qquad$ $\$3, \$5, -\$2, -\$4, \$6$

Find the value of the stock at the end of the next week.

Subtracting Integers

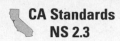
CA Standards
NS 2.3

Goal: Subtract integers.

Subtracting Integers

Words To subtract an integer, add its ⬚ .

Numbers $5 - 7 = 5 +$ ⬚   **Algebra** $a - b = a +$ ⬚

EXAMPLE 1 **Subtracting Integers**

> Need help with finding opposites? See page 129 of your textbook.

a. $4 - 9 = 4 +$ ⬚   To subtract 9, add its opposite, ⬚ .

   $=$ ⬚   Use rule for adding integers.

b. $-3 - 7 = -3 +$ ⬚   To subtract 7, add its opposite, ⬚ .

   $=$ ⬚   Use rule for adding integers.

c. $15 - (-4) = 15 +$ ⬚   To subtract -4, add its opposite, ⬚ .

   $=$ ⬚   Use rule for adding integers.

d. $-12 - (-7) = -12 +$ ⬚   To subtract -7, add its opposite, ⬚ .

   $=$ ⬚   Use rule for adding integers.

Guided Practice Find the difference.

1. $7 - 2$	**2.** $-4 - (-7)$	**3.** $-2 - 1$	**4.** $12 - (-9)$

EXAMPLE **2** **Multiple Choice Practice**

Diving A snorkeler explores the Great Barrier Reef at 3 feet below sea level. A diver explores the reef at 27 feet below sea level. What is the difference between these elevations?

Ⓐ 21 feet　　　Ⓑ 24 feet　　　Ⓒ 27 feet　　　Ⓓ 30 feet

Solution

Find the difference of -3 and -27 feet.

$$\boxed{} - \boxed{} = \boxed{} \qquad \text{Rule for subtracting integers}$$

$$= \boxed{} \qquad \text{Add.}$$

The difference between the elevations is $\boxed{}$ feet.

Answer: The correct answer is $\boxed{}$. Ⓐ Ⓑ Ⓒ Ⓓ

EXAMPLE **3** **Finding a Change in Temperature**

Weather In Spearfish, South Dakota, weather observers recorded the fa[...] change in temperature. In two minutes' time, the temperature changed f[...] $-20°C$ to $7°C$. What was the change in temperature?

Solution

$$\text{Change in temperature} = \boxed{} \text{ temperature} - \boxed{} \text{ temperature}$$

$$= \boxed{} - \boxed{} \qquad \text{Substitute values.}$$

$$= \boxed{} + \boxed{} \qquad \text{Rule for subtracting intege[...]}$$

$$= \boxed{} \qquad \text{Add.}$$

Answer: The change in temperature was $\boxed{}$ °C, so the temperature rose $\boxed{}$ °C.

Guided Practice **Solve the following problems.**

Homework

5. Find the difference between an elevation of 620 feet above sea level [...] an elevation of 15 feet below sea level.

6. The temperature at 7 A.M. was $-4°F$. At 7 P.M. the temperature was [...] $-18°F$. What was the change in temperature?

Process Diagram

For practicing notetaking skills

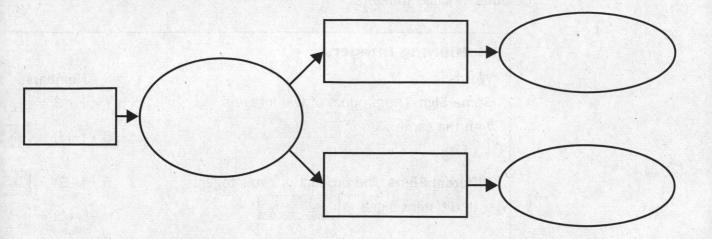

Multiplying Integers

Goal: Multiply integers.

Multiplying Integers

Words	Numbers
Same Sign The product of two integers with the same sign is [____].	$5 \cdot 3 = $ [__]
	$-5 \cdot (-3) = $ [__]
Different Signs The product of two integers with different signs is [____].	$5 \cdot (-3) = $ [__]
	$-5 \cdot 3 = $ [__]
Zero The product of an integer and 0 is [_].	$5 \cdot 0 = $ [__]
	$-5 \cdot 0 = $ [__]

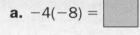 **Multiplying Integers**

You can also represent multiplication using parentheses.
$3(8) = 3 \cdot 8 = 3 \times 8$

a. $-4(-8) = $ [__]   The product of two integers with the same s
is [____].

b. $-9(3) = $ [__]   The product of two integers with different sig
is [____].

c. $-1(0) = $ [_]   The product of an integer and 0 is [__].

Guided Practice Find the product.

1. 7(5)	**2.** −2(−6)	**3.** 6(−6)	**4.** −8(8)	**5.** 0(−2

EXAMPLE 2 **Evaluating Variable Expressions**

Evaluate $-4 \cdot (-b)$ when $b = 7$.

Solution

$-4 \cdot (-b) = -4 \cdot \boxed{} \cdot b$　　　Rewrite $-b$ as $\boxed{} \cdot b$.

$ = \boxed{}$　　　Substitute $\boxed{}$ for b.

$ = \boxed{}$　　　Multiply $\boxed{}$ and $\boxed{}$.

$ = \boxed{}$　　　Multiply $\boxed{}$ and $\boxed{}$.

EXAMPLE 3 **Using Integer Multiplication**

After-School Business Chris withdraws $5 from his savings account every day for 6 days to invest the money in his after-school business. Use multiplication to find the change in his balance after those 6 days.

Solution

You can find the total change in the account balance by multiplying the daily balance change by the number of days of withdrawals.

Change in balance $= \boxed{} \left(\boxed{} \right) = \boxed{}$

Answer: The account balance will decrease $\$\boxed{}$.

Guided Practice Evaluate the expression when $a = -4$.

6. $9 \cdot (-a)$

7. $-a \cdot (-6)$

8. In Example 3, what is the change in Chris' balance after 8 days?

Dividing Integers

CA Stand
NS 2.

Goal: Divide integers.

Vocabulary

Mean:

Dividing Integers

Words   **Numbers**

Same Sign The quotient of two integers with the same sign is ☐.

$14 \div 2 =$ ☐

$\dfrac{-16}{-4} =$ ☐

> **WATCH OUT!**
> You cannot divide a number by 0. Any number divided by 0 is *undefined*. For example, $8 \div 0 = \underline{?}$ can be rewritten as $\underline{?} \cdot 0 = 8$. No number times 0 will result in a nonzero product.

Different Signs The quotient of two integers with different signs is ☐.

$25 \div (-5) =$ ☐

$\dfrac{-32}{8} =$ ☐

Zero The quotient of 0 and any nonzero integer is ☐.

$0 \div 13 =$ ☐

$\dfrac{0}{-11} =$ ☐

EXAMPLE 1   **Multiple Choice Practice**

What is the value of $36 \div (-9)$?

  (A) -45 (B) -4 (C) 4   (D) 45

Solution   Divide ☐ by ☐.

$36 \div (-9) = -4$

The quotient of two integers with different signs is ☐.

Answer: The correct answer is ☐.   (A)   (B)   (C)   (D)

EXAMPLE 2   **Dividing Integers**

a. $\dfrac{-50}{-10} =$ ☐   The quotient of two integers with the same sign is ☐.

The quotient of 0 and any nonzero integer is ☐.

b. $0 \div (-14) =$ ☐   is ☐.

---

1. $-18 \div 9$	**2.** $\dfrac{0}{-6}$	**3.** $\dfrac{-30}{-2}$	**4.** $22 \div (-1)$

EXAMPLE 3 **Finding a Mean**

Wall Street Stock brokers for a Wall Street firm tracked the changes in stock prices of the market over a 5-day period. Find the mean change in stock prices.

Day	Change in Market Value
Monday	$60
Tuesday	−$17
Wednesday	$23
Thursday	−$45
Friday	$19

Solution

The mean is calculated by finding the sum of the stock price changes and then dividing by the number of days.

Mean = [   ] = [   ]

Answer: The mean change in stock prices is $[   ].

Guided Practice Solve the following problem.

5. The low temperature was recorded over several hours' time. Find the mean of the temperatures.

$-15°F, -8°F, 2°F, 0°F, -4°F, 19°F$

nework

Order of Operations

Goal: Evaluate expressions involving two or more operations.

Vocabulary

Order of operations:

Order of Operations

1. Evaluate expressions ⬚.

2. Evaluate ⬚.

3. ⬚ from left to right.

4. ⬚ from left to right.

EXAMPLE 1 **Following Order of Operations**

Babysitting You earn spending money by babysitting. You charge $5 per hour plus a flat fee of $2 per child. Find the amount you earned babysitting 1 child for 4 hours.

$2 + 5 \times 4 =$ ⬚   First multiply ⬚ and ⬚.

          $=$ ⬚   Then add ⬚ and ⬚.

Answer: You earned $ ⬚.

Guided Practice **Evaluate the expression.**

1. $8 + 3 \times 4$	**2.** $32 - 3^3 \div 9$	**3.** $8 \times 4 + 5^2$

EXAMPLE 2 Using the Left-to-Right Rule

a. $15 - 8 + 9 - 3 = $ [____]   Subtract [__] from [__].

$= $ [____]   Add [__] and [__].

$= $ [__]   Subtract [__] from [__].

b. $100 \div \frac{2}{7} \div 2.5 = 100 \times \frac{7}{2} \div 2.5$ Multiply by [____].

$= $ [____]   Multiply [__] and [__].

$= $ [__]   Divide [__] by [__].

EXAMPLE 3 Multiple Choice Practice

What is the value of $17 + 3 \times 8 - 9$?

(A) -20 **(B)** -16 **(C)** 32 **(D)** 151

Solution

$17 + 3 \times 8 - 9 = $ [____]   Multiply [__] and [__].

$= $ [____]   Add [__] and [__].

$= $ [__]   Subtract [__] from [__].

Answer: The correct answer is [__].   **(A)**   **(B)**   **(C)**   **(D)**

Guided Practice Evaluate the expression.

4. $25 - 10 + 3 - 5$	**5.** $\dfrac{2}{3} \div 8 \times 4$	**6.** $-9 + 4 \times 5 - 12$

EXAMPLE 4 **Using Grouping Symbols**

Thinking of the letters PEMDAS might help you remember the order of operations:

Parentheses
Exponents
Multiplication
Division
Addition
Subtraction

a. $6(10 - 5) =$ [ ]   Subtract [ ] from [ ].

$=$ [ ]   Multiply [ ] and [ ].

b. $\dfrac{6 \cdot 6}{8 + 4} = \dfrac{\boxed{}}{\boxed{}}$ Multiply [ ] and [ ]. Add [ ] and

$=$ [ ]   Divide [ ] by [ ].

c. $(4 + 7)^2 - 20 =$ [ ]   Add [ ] and [ ].

$=$ [ ]   Evaluate the power.

$=$ [ ]   Subtract [ ] from [ ].

Guided Practice **Evaluate the expression.**

Homework

7. $2(14 - 4) + 7$	**8.** $(9 - 4)(5 - 2)^3$	**9.** $\dfrac{9 + 5}{63 \div 9}$

Process Diagram

For use with homework

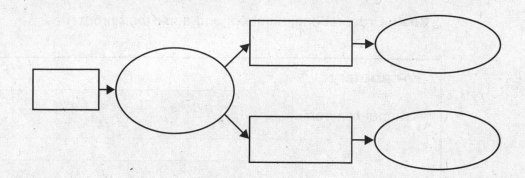

Rational Numbers and their Properties

CA Stand
NS 1.
AF 1.3

Goal: Order rational numbers and apply their properties.

Vocabulary

Rational number:

Additive inverse:

Additive identity:

Multiplicative inverse:

Multiplicative identity:

EXAMPLE 1 **Identifying Rational Numbers**

Show that the number is rational by writing it in $\frac{a}{b}$ form.

a. $12 =$ ⬚   **b.** $-\frac{1}{2} =$ ⬚   **c.** $0.6 =$ ⬚   **d.** $-1\frac{1}{12} =$

The negative sign in a negative fraction usually appears in front of the fraction bar. However, it can also appear in the numerator or in the denominator.

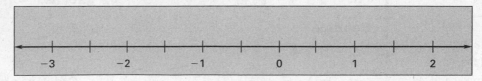

EXAMPLE 2 **Ordering Rational Numbers**

Order -2, -2.4, $1\frac{4}{5}$, $-1\frac{1}{4}$, and $-2\frac{4}{5}$ from least to greatest.

Graph each number on a number line.

−3	−2	−1	0	1	2	

Answer: From least to greatest, the numbers are:

Guided Practice Show that each number is rational by writing it in $\frac{a}{b}$ form. Then order the numbers from least to greatest.

1. 1.6, -6, $-\frac{6}{7}$, -0.7

2. $5\frac{1}{4}$, -4.5, $-4\frac{4}{5}$, 0

Commutative and Associative Properties

To remember the commutative property, remember that *commuters* are people who *move* or travel. To remember the associative property, remember that the people you *associate* with are the friends in your group.

Commutative Property of Addition

Words In a sum, you can add terms in any order.

Numbers $5 + (-6) = \boxed{} + \boxed{}$

Algebra $a + b = \boxed{} + \boxed{}$

Commutative Property of Multiplication

Words In a product, you can multiply factors in any order.

Numbers $4(-7) = \boxed{}\left(\boxed{}\right)$

Algebra $ab = \boxed{}$

Associative Property of Addition

Words Changing the grouping of terms will not change the sum.

Numbers

$(9 + 8) + 6 = \boxed{} + \left(\boxed{} + \boxed{}\right)$

Algebra

$(a + b) + c = \boxed{} + \left(\boxed{} + \boxed{}\right)$

Associative Property of Multiplication

Words Changing the grouping of factors will not change the product.

Numbers

$(2 \cdot 3) \cdot 4 = \boxed{} \cdot \left(\boxed{} \cdot \boxed{}\right)$

Algebra

$(ab)c = \boxed{}\left(\boxed{}\right)$

EXAMPLE **3** **Using Familiar Properties**

Evaluate the expression. Justify each step.

a. $-5 + 4 + (-7)$ **b.** $-20(12)(-5)$

Solution

a. $-5 + 4 + (-7)$

$= [-5 + 4] + (-7)$		Order of operations
$= \boxed{} + (-7)$		Commutative property of addi
$= \boxed{} + \boxed{}$		Associative property of additi
$= \boxed{} + \boxed{} = \boxed{}$		Add $\boxed{}$ and $\boxed{}$, then $\boxed{}$ and $\boxed{}$.

b. $-20(12)(-5)$

$= \boxed{}$		Order of operations
$= \boxed{} (-5)$		Commutative property of multiplic
$= \boxed{}$		Associative property of multiplicat
$= \boxed{} = \boxed{}$		Multiply $\boxed{}$ and $\boxed{}$, then $\boxed{}$ and $\boxed{}$.

> Using the order of operations, you would normally add -5 and 4 first. Using properties to reorder and regroup can make the calculations easier.

Guided Practice   Evaluate the expression. Justify each step.

3. $2.6 + [(-5) + 3.4]$

4. $5(-12)(2)$

5. $-8(9)(-5)$

Inverse and Identity Properties

Inverse Property of Addition	**Inverse Property of Multiplication**
Words The sum of a number and its additive inverse, or opposite, is ☐ .	**Words** The product of a nonzero number and its multiplicative inverse, or reciprocal, is ☐ .
Numbers $7 + (-7) = $ ☐	**Numbers** $\frac{2}{3} \cdot \frac{3}{2} = $ ☐
Algebra $a + (-a) = $ ☐	**Algebra** For nonzero integers a and b, $\frac{a}{b} \cdot \frac{b}{a} = $ ☐ .
Identity Property of Addition	**Identity Property of Multiplication**
Words The sum of a number and the additive identity, 0, is ☐ .	**Words** The product of a number and the multiplicative identity, 1, is ☐ .
Numbers $-9 + 0 = $ ☐	**Numbers** $3 \cdot 1 = $ ☐
Algebra $a + 0 = $ ☐	**Algebra** $a \cdot 1 = $ ☐

EXAMPLE 4 Using Properties

$10 + 3 + (-10) = $ ☐ $+ (-10)$ — Order of operations

$= $ ☐ $+ (-10)$ — Commutative property of addition

$= 3 + $ ☐ — Associative property of addition

$= $ ☐ $+$ ☐ — Inverse property of addition

$= $ ☐ — Identity property of addition

Guided Practice **Evaluate the expression. Justify each step.**

6. $66 + 102 + (-66)$

7. $4 \cdot 18 \cdot \frac{1}{4}$

8. $\frac{7}{8} \times \frac{3}{5} \times \frac{5}{3}$

Homework

The Distributive Property

CA Standards
AF 1.3

Goal: Apply the distributive property.

Vocabulary

Equivalent expressions:

EXAMPLE 1 **Writing Equivalent Expressions**

Tea Party A tea party has two rectangular tables: one that is 6 feet by 5 feet, and one that is 6 feet by 4 feet. What two expressions could be used to find the total area of the tables?

Solution

Need help with finding area? See page 684 in your text book.

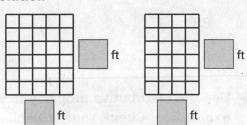

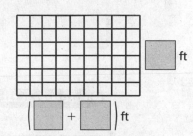

Area = [ ] + [ ]   Area = [ ]

= [ ] + [ ] = [ ] ft²   = [ ] = [ ] ft²

The Distributive Property

Algebra For all numbers a, b, and c, $a(b + c) =$ [ ] $+$ [ ] and

$a(b - c) =$ [ ] $-$ [ ].

Numbers $8(10 + 4) =$ [ ] $+$ [ ] and $3(4 - 2) =$ [ ] $-$ [ ]

EXAMPLE **2** **Writing Equivalent Expressions**

Use the distributive property to write an equivalent expression. Check your answer.

a. −6(2 + 7)   **b.** 3(75 − 25)   **c.** 8(2) + 8(9)

Solution

a.   −6(2 + 7) = [____] + [____]   Distributive property

Check: −6(9) $\stackrel{?}{=}$ [____] + [____]   Simplify.

−54 = [____] ✓   Answer checks.

b.   3(75 − 25) = [____] − [____]   Distributive property

Check: 3(50) $\stackrel{?}{=}$ [____] − [____]   Simplify.

150 = [____] ✓   Answer checks.

c.   8(2) + 8(9) = [____]   Distributive property

Check: 16 + 72 $\stackrel{?}{=}$ [____]   Simplify.

88 = [____] ✓   Answer checks.

WATCH OUT!

When using the distributive property, remember to multiply the outside number by both numbers inside the parentheses.

Guided Practice Use the distributive property to write an equivalent expression. Check your answer.

1. $5\left(\dfrac{1}{4}\right) + 5\left(\dfrac{3}{4}\right)$	**2.** −4(7 + 5)
3. 9(15 − 8)	**4.** 10(6) − 10(2)

EXAMPLE 3 **Using the Distributive Property**

Scrapbooks Leslie is making a scrapbook for her mother's birthday. She bought 6 packs of stickers for $6.95 each. Use the distributive property to find the total cost of the stickers.

Solution

$6(6.95) = $ [　　　]　　　　　　Write 6.95 as difference of a whole

number and a decimal.

$= $ [　　] $-$ [　　]　　　　Distributive property

$= $ [　　] $-$ [　　] $= $ [　　]　　Multiply. Then subtract.

Answer: The total cost of the stickers is $ [　　].

EXAMPLE 4 **Justifying Steps Using Properties**

Evaluate the expression $19(-5) + 19(6) - 8$ and justify your steps.

Solution

$19(-5) + 19(6) - 8 = $ [　　　] $- 8$　　Distributive property

$= $ [　　] $- 8$　　　　Order of operations

$= $ [　　] $- 8$　　　　Identity property of
multiplication

$= $ [　　]　　　　　Subtract [　] from [　].

Guided Practice

5. Suppose in Example 3 that each pack of stickers costs $5.90. Find the total cost of the stickers.

6. Evaluate the expression $4 + 10(3) + 10(-3)$ and justify your steps.

mework

Process Diagram

For use with homework

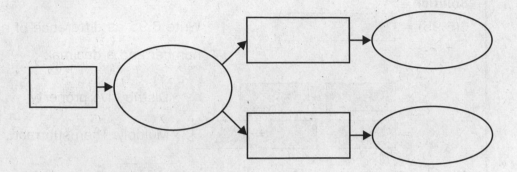

Words to Review

Give an example of the vocabulary word.

Integer

Negative integer

Positive integer

Opposite

Absolute value

Order of Operations

Rational number

Additive inverse

Additive identity

Multiplicative inverse

Multiplicative identity

Equivalent expressions

Review your notes and Chapter 3 by using the Chapter Review on pages 182–186 of your textbook.

Evaluating Expressions

Goal: Evaluate algebraic expressions.

EXAMPLE 1 **Evaluating Algebraic Expressions**

a. Evaluate $\frac{y}{3}$ when $y = 0.9$.

b. Evaluate $x^2 + 5$ when $x = 1$.

c. Evaluate $-2b - 4$ when $b = -6$.

Solution

a. $\frac{y}{3} = \boxed{}$ Substitute $\boxed{}$ for

      $= \boxed{}$ Divide.

b. $x^2 + 5 = \boxed{}$ Substitute $\boxed{}$ for x.

      $= \boxed{}$ Evaluate the power.

      $= \boxed{}$ Add.

c. $-2b - 4 = \boxed{}$ Substitute $\boxed{}$ for

      $= \boxed{}$ Multiply.

      $= \boxed{}$ Subtract.

WATCH OUT!
Be careful when using the multiplication symbol $\times$ in an algebraic expression. It can be confused with the variable x.

Guided Practice Evaluate the expression when $x = -5$ and $y = 2.5$.

1. $y - 1.9$	**2.** $\frac{3x}{4}$	**3.** $2x^2 + 21$

EXAMPLE 2 Evaluating with Two or More Variables

a. Evaluate $x^2 + y$ when $x = -4$ and $y = 3$.

b. Evaluate $\dfrac{-a + 7}{2b}$ when $a = 5$ and $b = 2$.

Solution

a. $x^2 + y = $ ☐   Substitute ☐ for x and ☐ for y.

  $= $ ☐   Evaluate the power.

  $= $ ☐   Add.

b. $\dfrac{-a + 7}{2b} = $ ☐   Substitute ☐ for a and ☐ for b.

  $= $ ☐   Add in numerator and multiply in denominator.

  $= $ ☐   Simplify.

Guided Practice Evaluate the expression when $a = 5$, $b = -2$, $c = 0.4$, and $d = 1.8$.

4. $a \cdot b$	**5.** $4c - 2d$	**6.** $b^2 + 8c$
7. $-a + 5c + d$	**8.** $\dfrac{3.4 + d}{b}$	**9.** $\dfrac{a - b}{c + 1}$

EXAMPLE 3 **Evaluating a Real-World Expression**

CDs Used CDs cost $7.50 each and new CDs cost $15.25 each. The t[...]
amount you spend on CDs is given by the expression $7.5x + 15.25y$,
where x is the number of used CDs you buy and y is the number of new
you buy. Find the amount you spend if you buy 5 used CDs and 2 new C[...]

Solution

Identify the values of the variables: $x = \boxed{}$ and $y = \boxed{}$.

$7.5x + 15.25y = \boxed{}$ Substitute

$= \boxed{}$ Multiply.

$= \boxed{}$ Add.

Answer: You spend $ $\boxed{}$.

> You can check
> the reasonableness
> of your answer in
> Example 3 by using
> estimation.
> $7.5(5) + 15.25(2)$
> $\approx 8(5) + 15(2)$
> $= 70$

Guided Practice **Solve the following problem.**

10. Cheerleading Your cheerleading squad earns 3 points for every jump[...]
10 points for every basket toss performed in a cheer. The total num[...]
of points your squad earns is given by the expression $3j + 10b$ whe[...]
the number of jumps and b is the number of basket tosses. Find the
total points earned if the squad performs 3 jumps and 4 basket
tosses.

Homework

Writing Expressions

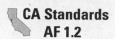
CA Standards
AF 1.2

Goal: Write algebraic expressions.

Vocabulary

Verbal model:

EXAMPLE 1 **Translating Verbal Phrases**

Verbal phrase	Expression
a. A number increased by 3	
b. 9 less than a number	
c. 1 more than three times a number	
d. 5 decreased by the quotient of a number and 2	

e phrase "the
rence of *a* and
written as *a* − *b*,
− *a*. The phrase
quotient of *a*
b" is written
as *a* ÷ *b*.

EXAMPLE 2 **Multiple Choice Practice**

It costs the art club $4.50 per person for a trip to the art museum. It costs the science club $5.90 per person for a trip to the science center. Which expression gives the difference between the cost for the science club's trip and the art club's trip where *a* is the number of art club members and *s* is the number of science club members?

A $4.5a − 5.9s$ **B** $1.4(s − a)$

C $5.9s + 4.5a$ **D** $5.9s − 4.5a$

Solution

The cost for the *s* science club members is [____]. The cost for the *a*

art club members is [____]. The difference is [____].

Answer: The correct answer is is [____]. Ⓐ Ⓑ Ⓒ Ⓓ

Write the verbal phrase as an algebraic expression. Let *n* represent the number.

1. 9 added to a number	**2.** $\frac{1}{4}$ of a number increased by 1
3. The difference of 24 divided by a number and 6.	**4.** 7 times the sum of a number squared and 5.

EXAMPLE 3 **Using a Verbal Model**

Pets You are stocking up on pet food for your pet-sitting business. Dog costs $6 per bag, cat food costs $3 per bag, and rabbit food costs $4 bag. You buy 4 bags of dog food, 3 bags of cat food, and 2 bags of rabb food. Write and evaluate an expression to find the total amount you spent on pet food.

Solution

Write a verbal model. Let *d* be the number of bags of dog food, *c* be the number of bags of cat food, and *r* be the number of bags of rabbit food.

> Use easy-to-remember variables to represent values. For instance, in Example 3, *d* represents the number of bags of dog food.

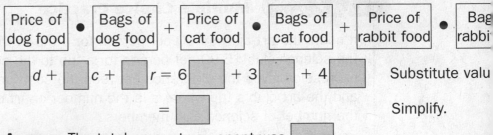

| Price of dog food | • | Bags of dog food | + | Price of cat food | • | Bags of cat food | + | Price of rabbit food | • | Bag rabbi |

☐ *d* + ☐ *c* + ☐ *r* = 6☐ + 3☐ + 4☐   Substitute valu

= ☐   Simplify.

Answer: The total amount you spent was ☐ .

Solve the following problem.

Homework

5. In Example 3, suppose you bought 2 bags of dog food, 4 bags of cat food, and 8 bags of rabbit food. Find the total amount you spent on pet food.

Copyright © by McDougal Littell, a division of Houghton Mifflin

Simplifying Expressions

Goal: Simplify expressions.

Vocabulary

Terms:

Coefficient:

Like terms:

Constant term:

EXAMPLE 1 **Coefficients, Like Terms, Constant Terms**

Identify the coefficients, like terms, and constant terms of the expression $x - 7 + 3x - 1$.

First, write the expression as a sum: $x + \left(\right) + 3x + \left(\right)$.

Coefficients: [ ]   Like terms: [ ] and [ ]

[ ] and [ ]

e coefficient x is 1. The coefficient −x is −1. ne expression can be written 2x − 1x, or + (−1x).

EXAMPLE 2 **Combining Like Terms**

Simplify the expression $8x - 2 + 4x$.

$8x - 2 + 4x = $ [ ]   Write expression as a sum.

$= (-2) + $ [ ]   Group like terms.

$= $ [ ]   Distributive property

$= $ [ ]   Simplify.

$= $ [ ]   Rewrite without parentheses.

commutative associative ties of addition ou to group like s after writing pression as a sum.

EXAMPLE 3 **Simplifying an Expression**

Simplify the expression $2(m - 1) + 6$.

$2(m - 1) + 6 =$	[ ]	Distributive property
$=$	[ ]	Write as a sum.
$=$	[ ]	Combine like terms.

Guided Practice Identify the coefficients, like terms, and constant terms of the expression. Then simplify the expression.

1. $-2n + 4 - 3n$	**2.** $10 - 6p + 5p - 4$	**3.** $3\ell + 9 - \ell - 6$

EXAMPLE 4 **Writing and Simplifying an Expression**

Gym Memberships A standard membership at a gym costs $10 a month. A deluxe membership costs $22 a month. Last month, 4 times as many people bought the standard membership than people who bought the deluxe membership. Write and simplify an expression for the amount of money made by the gym last month. How much money did the gym make if 6 people bought a deluxe membership?

Solution

Write a verbal model. Let p represent the number of people who bought a deluxe membership.

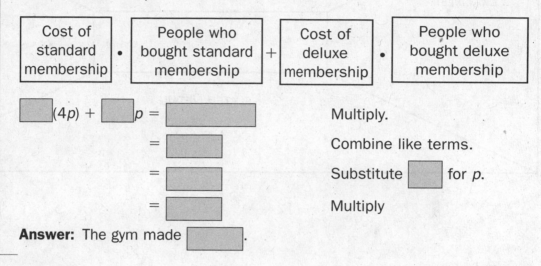

| Cost of standard membership | • | People who bought standard membership | + | Cost of deluxe membership | • | People who bought deluxe membership |

$\boxed{}(4p) + \boxed{}p = \boxed{}$ Multiply.

$= \boxed{}$ Combine like terms.

$= \boxed{}$ Substitute $\boxed{}$ for p.

$= \boxed{}$ Multiply

Answer: The gym made $\boxed{}$.

Guided Practice Solve the following problem.

4. In Example 4, suppose that 9 people bought a deluxe membership. How much did the gym make?

nework

Information Frame

For practicing notetaking skills

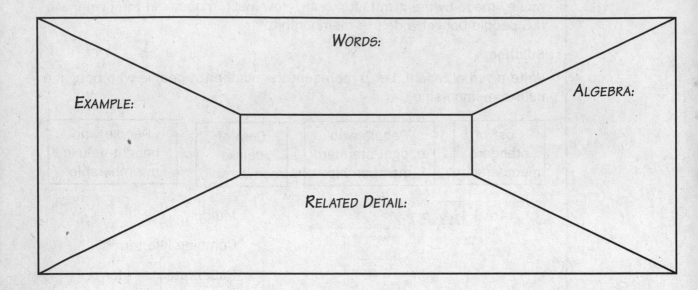

WORDS:

EXAMPLE:

ALGEBRA:

RELATED DETAIL:

4.4

Using Familiar Formulas

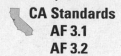
Goal: Use variables to express formulas.

Vocabulary

Equation:

Formula:

Perimeter and Area Formulas

	Diagram	Perimeter	Area
Rectangle	w, ℓ	$P = \boxed{} + 2w$	$A = \boxed{}$
Square	s, s	$P = \boxed{}$	$A = \boxed{}$

EXAMPLE 1 **Expressing Perimeter and Area**

Write and simplify expressions for the perimeter and area of the rectangle.

Solution

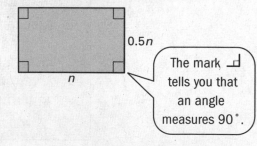

$0.5n$

n

> The mark ⌐ tells you that an angle measures 90°.

> Remember that perimeter is measured in linear units and area is measured in square units.

Perimeter of rectangle

$P = \boxed{} + \boxed{}$ Write formula.

$= \boxed{}(\boxed{}) + \boxed{}(\boxed{})$ Substitute.

$= \boxed{}$ Simplify.

Area of rectangle

$A = \boxed{}$ Write formula.

$= (\boxed{})(\boxed{})$ Substitute.

$= \boxed{}$ Simplify.

EXAMPLE 2 **Multiple Choice Practice**

A square with a side length of m is inside a square with a side of 6, as pictured at the right. Which expression represents the area of the shaded region in terms of m?

Ⓐ $36 - m^2$ Ⓑ $36 + m^2$

Ⓒ $36 - 2m$ Ⓓ $24 + 4m$

6

Solution

The area of the shaded region is equal to the area of the large squar[e]

[ ] the area of the small square. The area of the large square

([ ])([ ]) = [ ] . The area of the small square is [ ] ([ ]) = [ ]

So, the area of the shaded region is [   ] .

Answer: The correct answer is [ ] . Ⓐ Ⓑ Ⓒ Ⓓ

Guided Practice Write and simplify expressions for the perimeter and a[rea]
of a rectangle with the given dimensions.

1. $\ell = 3$, $w = x + 1$	**2.** $\ell = 2.4x$, $w = x$

3. A square with a side length of p is inside a rectangle with a length of 12 and a width of 5, as shown at the right. Write an expression that represents the area of the shaded region in terms of p.

p
p
12

Fomula Relating Distance, Rate, and Time

Words The distance travelled d is the [ ] of the constant or average rate r and the time t.

Algebra $d =$ [ ] $\cdot$ [ ] or $d =$ [ ]

Numbers $d = \dfrac{20 \text{ miles}}{\text{hour}} \cdot 4 \text{ hours} =$ [ ]

EXAMPLE 3 **Using Formula for Distance**

Biking Holly bikes at a steady rate of 3.1 miles per hour for h hours and takes a break. She then bikes for 6 more miles. Write an expression for the total distance she bikes.

Solution

Step 1 Use the formula for distance to find the distance Holly bikes before the break.

$d =$ [ ] $\cdot$ [ ]   Write formula for distance.

$=$ [ ] $\cdot$ [ ]   Substitute [ ] for r and [ ] for t.

Step 2 Add the distance she bikes after the break [ ] $+$ [ ].

Answer: The total distance Holly bikes is ([ ] $+$ [ ]) miles.

Guided Practice Solve.

4. How far does an airplane travel in 3 hours at a rate of 450 miles per hour?

Temperature Conversions

Words

Convert [　　　] to Fahrenheit

Convert [　　　　] to Celsius

Formulas

$F = \boxed{} C + \boxed{}$

Numbers

$\boxed{} = \frac{9}{5}(20) + 32$

$C = \frac{5}{9}(F - \boxed{})$

$\boxed{} = \frac{5}{9}(68 - 32)$

EXAMPLE 4 **Converting a Temperature**

Convert 25°C to Fahrenheit.

Solution

$F = \boxed{}$ ⟶ Write formula for degrees Fahren[heit]

$= \boxed{}$ ⟶ Substitute $\boxed{}$ for C.

$= \boxed{}$ ⟶ Multiply.

$= \boxed{}$ ⟶ Add.

Answer: The temperature 25°C is equal to $\boxed{}$

> You can check your answer to Example 4 by substituting 77 for F in the formula $C = \frac{5}{9}(F - 32)$ and showing that $C = 25$.

Homework

Guided Practice Convert the temperature from degrees Fahrenheit to degrees Celsius or from degrees Celsius to degrees Fahrenheit.

5. 40°C	**6.** 86°F	**7.** 59°F	**8.** 10°C

Equations and Mental Math

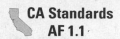

CA Standards
AF 1.1

Goal: Use mental math to solve an equation.

Vocabulary

Solution:

Solving an equation:

EXAMPLE 1   **Checking Possible Solutions**

Tell whether the number is a solution of $f + 7 = 13$.

    a. $f = 8$ **b.** $f = 6$

Symbol	Meaning
$=$	is equal to
$\stackrel{?}{=}$	is equal to ?
$\neq$	is not equal to

Solution

a. $f + 7 = 13$ Write original equation.

           Substitute [ ] for f.

           The equation [ ] true, .

b. $f + 7 = 13$ Write original equation.

           Substitute [ ] for f.

           The equation [ ] true, .

Guided Practice   **Tell whether the number is a solution of the equation.**

1. $4t = 20$; $t = 6$	**2.** $17 - p = 12$; $p = 5$	**3.** $12 \div d = 4$; $d = 3$

EXAMPLE 2 **Translating Verbal Sentences**

Verbal sentence   **Equation**

a. 12 increased by a number is 18.

b. The difference of a number and 6 equals −2.

c. The product of $\frac{2}{3}$ and a number is 15.

d. −2 is equal to five times the sum of a number and 3.

Guided Practice Write the verbal sentence as an equation. Let *n* repre the number.

4. 24 divided by a number equals 6.	**5.** 26 minus 4 times a number i

EXAMPLE 3 **Using Mental Math to Solve Equations**

Equation ⟶ Question ⟶ Solution ⟶ Check

a. $5 + v = 9$ ▢ plus ▢
equals ▢ ?   ▢ ▢

b. $s - 7 = 4$ ▢
minus ▢ equals ▢ ?   ▢ ▢

c. $5h = 35$ ▢ times ▢
equals ▢ ?   ▢ ▢

d. $j \div 6 = 8$ ▢ divided
by ▢ equals ▢ ?   ▢ ▢

Guided Practice Solve the equation using mental math.

6. $2n = 18$	**7.** $22 = k - 8$	**8.** $4 + r = 17$	**9.** $56 \div w = 8$

EXAMPLE 4 **Using an Area Formula**

What is the length of a rectangle that has a width of 8 meters and an area of 72 square meters?

Solution

[   ]   Write formula for area of a rectangle.

[   ] = [   ]   Substitute [   ] for *A* and [   ] for *w*.

[   ] = [   ]   Use mental math to solve the equation.

Answer: The length of the rectangle is [   ] meters.

EXAMPLE 5 **Using Formula for Distance**

Race Walker A race walker travels at a speed of 5 miles per hour. She tallies her training schedule and finds that she walked 100 miles this month. How much time did she spend walking this month?

Solution

[   ]   Write formula for distance.

[   ] = [   ]   Substitute [   ] for *d* and [   ] for *r*.

[   ] = [   ]   Use mental math to solve equation.

Answer: She walked [   ] hours this month.

Guided Practice **Solve the following problems.**

10. What is the width of a rectangle that has a lenght of 12 inches and an a of 36 square inches?

11. A high speed passenger commuter ferry is advertised as being able to r a 16 mile crossing between land and an island in only 48 minutes. How many minutes does it take the ferry to travel 1 mile?

Information Frame

For use with homework

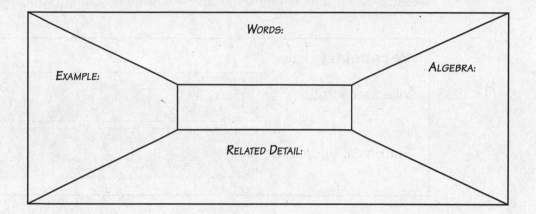

Solving Addition and Subtraction Equations

Goal: Solve addition and subtraction equations using properties.

Vocabulary

Inverse operation:

Equivalent equations:

Subtraction Property of Equality

Words Subtracting the same number from each side of an equation

produces an [_____] equation.

Algebra $x + a = b$ $\longrightarrow$ $x + a - a = b$ [___] [___]

EXAMPLE 1 **Solving an Addition Equation**

Solve $x + 3 = -1$.

$x + 3 = -1$ Write original equation.

[___] [___]

[___] = [___]

                             from each side.

Simplify.

[___]

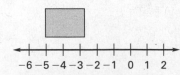

$-6\ -5\ -4\ -3\ -2\ -1\ \ 0\ \ 1\ \ 2$

✓ **Check** $x + 3 = -1$ Write original equation.

[___] $\overset{?}{=}$ [___]   Substitute [___] for x.

[_____] ✓   Solution checks.

Addition Property of Equality

Words Adding the same number to each side of an equation produces an [_____] equation.

Algebra $x - a = b$ $\longrightarrow$ $x - a + a = b$ [ ] [ ]

EXAMPLE 2 **Solving a Subtraction Equation**

Solve $-4 = y - 9$.

$$-4 = y - 9$$ Write original equation.

[ ] = [ ]   [ ] to each side.

[ ] = [ ]   Simplify.

✓ **Check** $-4 = y - 9$ Write original equation.

[ ] $\overset{?}{=}$ [ ]   Substitute [ ] for y.

[ ] ✓   Solution checks.

EXAMPLE 3 **Combining Like Terms**

Solve $7 = 4.1 + b + 1$.

$$7 = 4.1 + b + 1$$ Write original equation.

[ ] $= 4.1 +$ [ ]   Group like terms.

[ ] = [ ]   Combine like terms.

[ ] = [ ]   [ ] from each side.

[ ] = [ ]   Simplify.

✓ **Check** $7 = 4.1 + b + 1$ Write original equation.

[ ] $\overset{?}{=}$ [ ]   Substitute [ ] for b.

[ ] ✓   Solution checks.

     Lesson 4.6 • **Course 1 Notetaking Guide**   **97**

Solve the equation. Graph and check your solution.

1. $t + 7 = 12$	**2.** $n + 8 = 0$	**3.** $6 = y - 4$
0 2 4 6 8 10 12 14 16	−10 −8 −6 −4 −2 0 2 4	6 7 8 9 10 11 12 13
4. $r - 12 = 15$	**5.** $p - (-3.6) = 4.9$	**6.** $2.7 + s - 1.9$
9 12 15 18 21 24 27 30 33	−1 0 1 2 3	2 3 4 5

EXAMPLE 4 **Writing and Solving an Equation**

Business Travel Carol is out of the office for 8 hours meeting with a cl
She spends 0.75 hour driving to the client's office, and 1.25 hours dri
back from the client's office. How long was Carol at the client's office?

Solution

Write a verbal model. Let h represent the number of hours Carol spent
at the client's office.

Time away
from office = [   ] + [   ] + [   ]

[   ] = [   ]   Write equation.

[   ] = [   ]   Combine like terms.

[   ] = [   ]   [   ] from each side.

[   ] = [   ]   Simplify.

Answer: Carol spent [   ] hours at the client's office.

Homework

Solving Multiplication and Division Equations

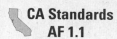

Goal: Solve multiplication and division equations.

Division Property of Equality

Words Dividing each side of an equation by the same nonzero number

produces an [   ] equation.

Algebra $ax = b \, (a \neq 0)$ ⟶ $\dfrac{ax}{a} =$ [   ]

EXAMPLE 1 **Solving a Multiplication Equation**

Solve $-30 = 6x$.

$-30 = 6x$ Write original equation.

$\dfrac{-30}{\boxed{}} = \dfrac{6x}{\boxed{}}$ [   ] each side by [   ].

$\boxed{} = \boxed{}$ Simplify.

Check $-30 = 6x$.   Write original equation.

$\boxed{} \stackrel{?}{=} \boxed{}$ Substitute [   ] for x.

$\boxed{}$ ✓   Solution checks.

Multiplication Property of Equality

Words Multiplying each side of an equation by the same nonzero number

produces an [   ] equation.

Algebra $\dfrac{x}{a} = b \, (a \neq 0)$ ⟶ $a \cdot \dfrac{x}{a} =$ [   ]

EXAMPLE 2

Solving a Division Equation

Solve $\frac{x}{4} = 0.3$.

$$\frac{x}{4} = 0.3 \qquad \text{Write original equation.}$$

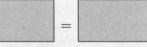 $=$ 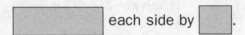 each side by ⬚.

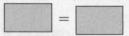 $=$ ⬚   Simplify.

EXAMPLE 3   **Solving an Equation Using a Reciprocal**

Solve $\frac{3}{4} x = -6$.

Need help with finding a reciprocal? See page 95 of your textbook.

$$\frac{3}{4} x = -6 \qquad \text{Write original equation.}$$

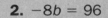 $=$ 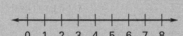   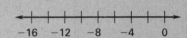 each side by ⬚.

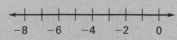 $=$ 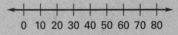   Simplify.

Guided Practice   **Solve the equation. Graph and check your solution.**

1. $9v = 36$	**2.** $-8b = 96$
0 1 2 3 4 5 6 7 8	-16 -12 -8 -4 0
3. $-1.7 = \frac{k}{3}$	**4.** $\frac{d}{4} = 15$
-8 -6 -4 -2 0	0 10 20 30 40 50 60 70 80
5. $6q - 4q = 16$	**6.** $\frac{5}{8} m = 10$
4 5 6 7 8 9 10 11 12	4 8 12 16 20 24 28 32 36

EXAMPLE 4 Multiple Choice Practice

Rollerblading A woman is rollerblading through the park. You measure a 75-foot stretch of sidewalk, and count that she skates that portion of the sidewalk in 12 seconds. Which equation can you use to find the speed r (in feet per second) of the woman?

(A) $75 = \frac{r}{12}$ (B) $12 = \frac{r}{75}$

(C) $75 = 12r$ (D) $12 = 75r$

Solution

$d = rt$ Write formula for distance.

$\boxed{} = \boxed{}$ Substitute $\boxed{}$ for d and $\boxed{}$ for t.

$\boxed{} = \boxed{}$ $\boxed{}$ each side by $\boxed{}$.

$\boxed{} = \boxed{}$ Simplify.

Answer: The speed of the woman is $\boxed{}$ feet per second. The equation used to find the speed is $\boxed{}$.

The correct answer is $\boxed{}$. (A)   (B)   (C)   (D)

Guided Practice Solve the following problem.

7. A filmmaker makes an edited version of his movie that is 120 minutes long. The unedited footage is 7 times as long as the edited version. Write and solve an equation to find the length of the unedited film.

Information Frame

For use with homework

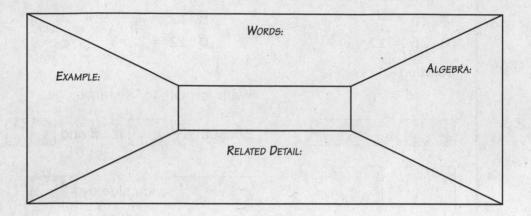

WORDS:

EXAMPLE:

ALGEBRA:

RELATED DETAIL:

Words to Review

Give an example of the vocabulary word.

Verbal model

Terms

Coefficient

Like terms

Constant term

Equation

Formula

Solution

Solving an equation

Inverse operations

Equivalent equations

Review your notes and Chapter 4 by using the Chapter Review on pages 243–246 of your textbook.

Ratios

Goal: Write and compare ratios.

Vocabulary

Ratio:

Equivalent ratios:

Writing a Ratio

Words	Numbers	Algebra
wins to losses	16 to 10	*a* to *b*, where *b* is nonzero
$\dfrac{\text{wins}}{\text{losses}}$		, where *b* is nonzero
wins : losses		, where *b* is nonzero.

EXAMPLE 1 **Writing a Ratio**

You can make comparisons about 6th grade students in first period class

Silverlake Middle School's 6th Grade		
Teacher	**Students in 1st Period**	**Students in 2nd Period**
Ms. Black	29	23
Mr. Henderson	24	27
Ms. Solomon	25	26
Mr. O'Grady	24	25

WATCH OUT!
Be sure that the first quantity in the ratio goes in the numerator and that the second quantity goes in the denominator.

a. Ms. Black's first period students to Mr. O'Grady's first period studer

Ms. Black = ☐ , Mr. O'Grady = ☐

Answer: ☐ , ☐ , or ☐

104   Lesson 5.1 • **Course 1 Notetaking Guide**

Copyright © by McDougal Littell, a division of Houghton Mifflin C

b. Ms. Solomon's first period students to all first period students

Ms. Solomon = [ ] ; all = [ ] = [ ]

Answer: [ ] , [ ] , or [ ]

Guided Practice Use the table on the previous page to write the ratios.

1. Ms. Black's 1st period students to Ms. Black's 2nd period students

2. All 1st period students to all 2nd period students

3. Mr. O'Grady's 2nd period students to all other 2nd period students

EXAMPLE 2 **Multiple Choice Practice**

Alicia spends 270 minutes cooking for a dinner party. The guests finish the meal in 30 minutes. What is the ratio of time spent cooking to time spent eating?

(A) 1 : 240   **(B)** 1 : 9   **(C)** 9 : 1   **(D)** 240 : 1

Solution

Write the ratio of time spent cooking to time spent eating.

$$\frac{\text{Time-cooking}}{\text{Time-eating}} = \boxed{} \qquad \text{Write ratio.}$$

$$= \boxed{} \qquad \text{Simplify ratio.}$$

Answer: The ratio of time spent cooking to time spent eating is [ ] : [ ] .

The correct answer is [ ] . **(A)** **(B)** **(C)** **(D)**

EXAMPLE 3 **Comparing Ratios**

Books Kylie and Sophia compared their book collections. To determine
has the greater ratio of mysteries to biographies, write the ratios.

	Mystery	**Fiction**	**Biography**
Kylie	12	6	15
Sophia	7	15	10

*Need help
with writing fractions
as decimals? See
page 40 of your
textbook.*

Kylie: $\dfrac{\text{mysteries}}{\text{biographies}} = \boxed{}$ **Sophia:** $\dfrac{\text{mysteries}}{\text{biographies}} = \boxed{}$ Write ra
as fracti

$= \boxed{}$ $= \boxed{}$ Write fra
as decir

Answer: Because $\boxed{} > \boxed{}$, $\boxed{}$ has the greater ratio of
mysteries to biographies.

Guided Practice **Refer to Example 3.**

4. Does Kylie or Sophia have a greater ratio of fiction to mystery books

5. Does Kylie or Sophia have a greater ratio of biography to fiction?

Homework

Rates

CA Standards
AF 2.2
AF 2.3
NS 1.2

Goal: Use rates to compare two quantities with different units.

Vocabulary

Rate: _____

Unit Rate: _____

EXAMPLE 1 Finding a Unit Rate

Microwave Cooking A microwave oven increases the temperature of a cup of water by 42°F in 14 seconds. What is the heating rate in degrees Fahrenheit per second?

Solution

First, write a rate comparing the temperature increase to the seconds it took to heat. Then rewrite the fraction so that the denominator is 1.

$$\frac{42°F}{14 \text{ sec}} = \frac{42°F \div \boxed{}}{14 \text{ sec} \div \boxed{}}$$ Divide numerator and denominator by $\boxed{}$.

$$= \boxed{}$$ Simplify.

Answer: The heating rate is about $\boxed{}$°F per second.

Guided Practice Find the unit rate.

1. $72 in 8 hours	**2.** 90 miles in 6 days	**3.** 4·cups in 10 servings

EXAMPLE 2 · Finding Average Speed

Family Vacation A family drove their car 429 miles in 8 hours and 15 minutes. What was the average speed of the car?

Solution

1. Rewrite the time so that the units are the same.

$$8 \text{ h} + 15 \text{ min} = 8 \text{ h} + \boxed{} \text{ h} = \boxed{} \text{ h}$$

2. Find the average speed.

$$\frac{429 \text{ miles}}{8.25 \text{ hours}} = \frac{429 \text{ miles} \div \boxed{}}{8.25 \text{ hours} \div \boxed{}} \qquad \text{Divide numerator and denominator by } \boxed{}$$

$$= \boxed{} \qquad \text{Simplify.}$$

Answer: The car's average speed was $\boxed{}$ miles per hour.

EXAMPLE 3 · Comparing Unit Rates

A unit price is a type of unit rate.

Cereal A store sells the same cereal the following two ways: a small 48-ounce package for $1.92 and a large 64-ounce package for $3.20. To determine which is the better buy, find the unit price for both types.

Small package: $\dfrac{\$1.92}{48 \text{ oz}} = \boxed{}$ Write as unit rate.

Large package: $\dfrac{\$3.20}{64 \text{ oz}} = \boxed{}$ Write as unit rate.

Answer: The $\boxed{}$ package of cereal is a better buy because it costs less per ounce.

Guided Practice · Solve the following problems.

Homework

4. It takes you 11 minutes and 40 seconds to ride your bike 2800 yards. What is your average speed in yards per second?

5. Which of the following is the better buy: 2 notebooks for $2.40 or 6 notebooks for $4.80?

Word Magnet

For practicing notetaking skills

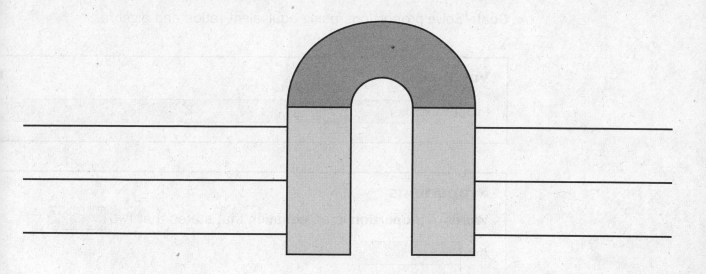

Writing and Solving Proportions

CA Standa
NS 1.3
AF 2.3

LESSON 5.3

Goal: Solve proportions using equivalent ratios and algebra.

Vocabulary

Proportion: ⬜

Proportions

Words A **proportion** is an equation that states that two ⬜

are ⬜ .

Numbers $\dfrac{\square}{\square} = \dfrac{\square}{\square}$ The proportion is read "4 is to 5 as 8 is to 10

Algebra $\dfrac{a}{b} = \dfrac{c}{d}$, where b and d are nonzero numbers.

EXAMPLE 1 **Solving Proportions Using Equivalent Ratio**

Skating Lessons A skating rink offers private skating lessons at a cost
$15 for 30 minutes. How much will it cost for 90 minutes of private less

Solution

To find the price paid P for 90 minutes of lessons, solve the
proportion $\dfrac{15}{30} = \dfrac{P}{90}$.

1. Ask yourself: What number can you multiply 30 by to get 90?

$$\dfrac{15}{30} = \dfrac{P}{90}$$

$\times$?

2. Because $30 \times \boxed{} = 90$, multiply the numerator by $\boxed{}$ to find P.

$$\times \boxed{}$$

$$\frac{15}{30} = \frac{P}{90}$$

$$\times \boxed{}$$

Answer: Because $15 \times \boxed{} = \boxed{}$, $P = \boxed{}$. So, the price of 90 minutes of private lessons is $\$\boxed{}$.

EXAMPLE 2 Solving Proportions Using Algebra

Solve the proportion $\dfrac{4}{14} = \dfrac{x}{21}$.

You can think of $\dfrac{x}{21}$ as $\dfrac{1}{21} \cdot x$ and use a multiplicative inverse to solve the proportion.

$$\frac{1}{1} \cdot \frac{4}{14} =$$
$$\frac{21}{1} \cdot \frac{1}{21} \cdot x$$
$$6 = x$$

$$\frac{4}{14} = \frac{x}{21} \qquad \text{Write original proportion.}$$

$$\boxed{} \cdot \frac{4}{14} = \boxed{} \cdot \frac{x}{21} \qquad \text{Multiply each side by } \boxed{}.$$

$$\frac{\boxed{}}{\boxed{}} = x \qquad \text{Simplify.}$$

$$\boxed{} = x \qquad \text{Simplify fraction.}$$

Answer: The solution is $\boxed{}$.

Guided Practice Use equivalent ratios to solve the proportion.

1. $\dfrac{2}{3} = \dfrac{z}{12}$	**2.** $\dfrac{4}{3} = \dfrac{x}{18}$	**3.** $\dfrac{30}{c} = \dfrac{5}{8}$	**4.** $\dfrac{4}{n} = \dfrac{48}{12}$

Use algebra to solve the proportion.

5. $\dfrac{4}{6} = \dfrac{m}{15}$	**6.** $\dfrac{10}{15} = \dfrac{n}{9}$	**7.** $\dfrac{h}{20} = \dfrac{6}{8}$	**8.** $\dfrac{b}{12} = \dfrac{3}{18}$

EXAMPLE **3** **Multiple Choice Practice**

Tyler plays basketball and scores an average of 10 points in 8 minutes playing time. How many points does Tyler average in 4 minutes of play?

Ⓐ 2   Ⓑ 3   Ⓒ 5   Ⓓ 6

Solution

1. Write a proportion. Let x represent the average number of points scored in 4 minutes.

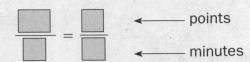

⟵ points

⟵ minutes

2. Solve the proportion.

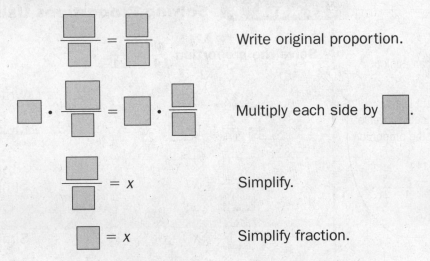

Write original proportion.

Multiply each side by ☐.

= x Simplify.

☐ = x Simplify fraction.

Answer: Tyler averages ☐ points in 4 minutes of playing time.

The correct answer is ☐   Ⓐ Ⓑ Ⓒ Ⓓ

WATCH OUT!

You cannot write a proportion that compares points to minutes and minutes to points.

$$\frac{points}{minutes} \neq \frac{minutes}{points}$$

Guided Practice Refer to Example 3

Homework

9. How many points does Tyler average in 20 minutes of play?

Solving Proportions Using Cross Products

CA Standards
NS 1.3
AF 2.2

Goal: Solve proportions using cross products.

Vocabulary

Cross products:

Cross Products Property

Words The cross products of a proportion are [ ].

Numbers

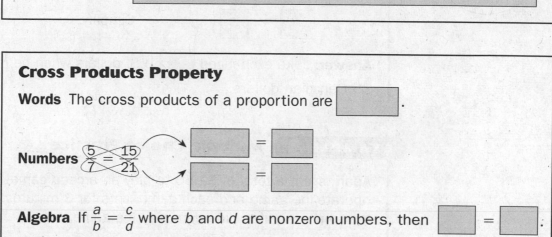

Algebra If $\frac{a}{b} = \frac{c}{d}$ where b and d are nonzero numbers, then [ ] = [ ].

EXAMPLE 1 **Solving a Proportion Using Cross Products**

Use the cross products property to solve $\frac{2}{5} = \frac{x}{7}$.

$\frac{2}{5} = \frac{x}{7}$ Write original proportion.

[ ] = [ ]   Use cross products property.

$\frac{[\ ]}{[\ ]} = \frac{[\ ]}{[\ ]}$ Divide each side by [ ].

[ ] = [ ]   Simplify.

e phrase
ss *products*
s from the "X"
formed by the
al numbers in
proportion.

EXAMPLE 2 **Writing and Solving a Proportion**

Currency Exchange When Jake visited Canada, he exchanged 10 U.S. dollars and he received 14 Canadian dollars. Find how many U.S. dollars he exchanged when he received 35 Canadian dollars.

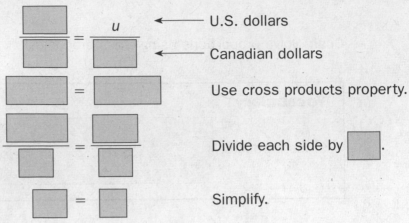

You can also find the number of U.S. dollars Jake exchanged by using an equivalent proportion such as:

$$\frac{14}{10} = \frac{35}{u}.$$

$\dfrac{\boxed{}}{\boxed{}} = \dfrac{u}{\boxed{}}$ ⟵ U.S. dollars ⟵ Canadian dollars

$\boxed{} = \boxed{}$ Use cross products property.

$\dfrac{\boxed{}}{\boxed{}} = \dfrac{\boxed{}}{\boxed{}}$ Divide each side by $\boxed{}$.

$\boxed{} = \boxed{}$ Simplify.

Answer: Jake exchanged $\boxed{}$ U.S. dollars when he received 35 Canadian dollars.

EXAMPLE 3 **Multiple Choice Practice**

Adam spent a total of $1.50 to play an arcade game. Two quarters operate the game and each game lasts for 3 minutes. At most, how many minutes did Adam play the game?

A 1.5 min   **B** 3 min   **C** 4 min   **D** 9 min

Solution

Step 1 **Convert** the money spent into quarters. Because 1 quarter equals $\boxed{}$, Adam used $\boxed{} \div \boxed{}$, or $\boxed{}$ quarters play the game.

Step 2 **Write** a proportion to find the greatest amount of time *t* (minutes) he played the game.

$\dfrac{\boxed{}}{\boxed{}} = \dfrac{\boxed{}}{\boxed{}}$ ⟵ Quarters ⟵ Time

$\boxed{} = \boxed{}$ Use cross products property

$\boxed{} = \boxed{}$ Simplify.

Answer: At most, Adam played the game for 9 minutes.

The correct answer is $\boxed{}$.   **A** **B** **C** **D**

EXAMPLE 4 Solve a Multi-Step Problem

Baseball The ratio of left-handed pitchers to right-handed pitchers on a baseball team is 2 to 5. If the team has 14 pitchers, how many are left-handed?

Solution

First, determine the ratio of left-handed pitchers to total pitchers.

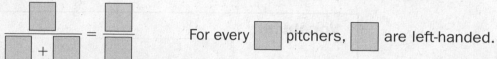

$$\frac{\boxed{}}{\boxed{} + \boxed{}} = \frac{\boxed{}}{\boxed{}}$$ For every $\boxed{}$ pitchers, $\boxed{}$ are left-handed.

To find the number ℓ of left-handed pitchers, set up a proportion and solve it.

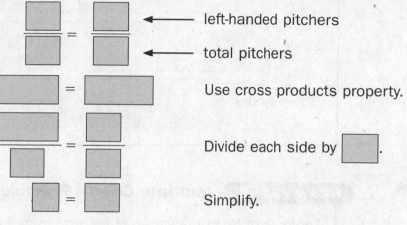

$\dfrac{\boxed{}}{\boxed{}} = \dfrac{\boxed{}}{\boxed{}}$ ← left-handed pitchers
  ← total pitchers

$\boxed{} = \boxed{}$ Use cross products property.

$\dfrac{\boxed{}}{\boxed{}} = \dfrac{\boxed{}}{\boxed{}}$ Divide each side by $\boxed{}$.

$\boxed{} = \boxed{}$ Simplify.

Answer: There are $\boxed{}$ left-handed pitchers on the team.

Guided Practice Solve the following problems.

1. In Example 2, if Jake exchanged 45 U.S. dollars, how many Canadian dollars would he receive?

2. A baseball team has a ratio of wins to losses of 5 to 3. If they played 24 games, how many games did they lose?

nework

Scale Drawings and Models

Goal: Use proportions to solve problems involving scale drawings and mo

Vocabulary

Scale drawing:

Scale:

Scale model:

EXAMPLE 1 **Multiple Choice Practice**

The map of Nebraska shown at the right uses a scale of 1.5 centimeters equals 100 miles. On the map, the distance between Ogallala and Central City is 3 centimeters. What is the actual distance between the tow

Ⓐ 0.045 mi   Ⓑ 22 mi   Ⓒ 50 mi   Ⓓ 200 mi

Solution

Write and solve a proportion to find the distance *d* between the towns.

$$\frac{\boxed{}}{\boxed{}} = \frac{\boxed{}}{\boxed{}}$$ ← centimeters
← miles

Neb

• Alliance

               Central City
      • Ogallala

                  • Geneva

1.5 cm :

$$\boxed{} = \boxed{}$$ Use cross products property.

$$\frac{\boxed{}}{\boxed{}} = \frac{\boxed{}}{\boxed{}}$$ Divide each side by $\boxed{}$.

$$\boxed{} = \boxed{}$$ Simplify.

Answer: The actual distance between Ogallala and Central City is about

$\boxed{}$ miles. The correct answer is $\boxed{}$. Ⓐ Ⓑ Ⓒ Ⓓ

1. Estimate the distance, in miles, between the towns of Alliance and Geneva.

EXAMPLE 2   Finding a Dimension on a Scale Model

Model Cars A scale model of an Austin Healy automobile is for sale at the local Hobby Shop. The scale used is 1 : 15. The height of the actual car is 45 inches. Find the height of the model.

Solution

Write and solve a proportion to find the height h of the model of the Austin Healy.

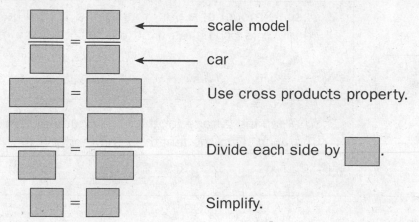

    ⟵ scale model

    ⟵ car

Use cross products property.

Divide each side by ☐ .

Simplify.

Answer: The height of the model is ☐ inches.

(margin note, left)
...hen a scale
...ten as a ratio, it
...y takes the form
...own below.

...ale . actual
...del ˙ object

EXAMPLE **3** **Finding a Scale**

Architecture An architect is planning a theater complex. The model is 3.75 feet tall. The resulting theater complex will be 150 feet tall. What is the model's scale?

Solution

Write a ratio. Then simplify.

scale model ⟶ □ / □ = □/□ ÷ □ = □/□ · □ = □/□

full size ⟶

Answer: The scale of the model is □ : □ .

Guided Practice **Solve the following problems.**

2. A scale model of a park fountain is 1 : 8. The height of the actual fountain is 60 inches. Find the height of the model.

Homework

3. The parking garage for the theater complex in Example 3 is 180 feet long. Find the length of the model.

Word Magnet

For use with homework

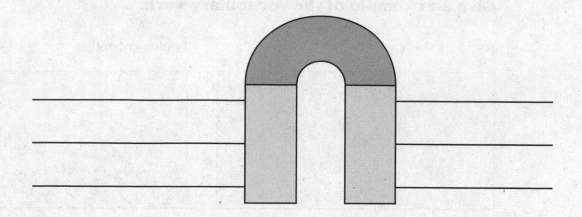

Words to Review

Give an example of the vocabulary word.

Ratio

Equivalent ratios

Rate

Unit rate

Proportion

Cross products

Scale drawing

Scale

Scale model

Review your notes and Chapter 5 by using the Chapter Review on pages 290–292 of your textbook.

LESSON 6.1

Percents and Fractions

 CA Stand
Gr. 5

Goal: Find the percent of a number.

Vocabulary

Percent: _____

Understanding Percent

> You can remember that percent means "per hundred" by thinking of how many cents are in a dollar.

The model at the right has 22 out of 100 squares shaded. You can say that [ ] percent of the squares are shaded.

Numbers You can write 22 percent as

[ ] or as [ ] %.

Algebra You can write *p* percent as

[ ] or as [ ] %.

[ ] percent

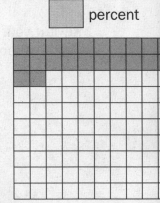

EXAMPLE 1 Writing Percents as Fractions

Write the percent as a fraction.

a. 49%   **b.** 60%

Solution

a. 49% = [ ]/[ ]   **b.** 60% = [ ]/[ ] = [ ]/[ ]

Write the percent as a fraction in simplest form.

1. 18%	**2.** 45%	**3.** 41%	**4.** 70%

EXAMPLE 2 **Writing Fractions as Percents**

To write a fraction as a percent, rewrite the fraction with a denominator of 100.

a. $\dfrac{3}{10} = \dfrac{3 \times \boxed{}}{10 \times \boxed{}} = \dfrac{\boxed{}}{\boxed{}} = \boxed{}\%$

b. $\dfrac{4}{5} = \dfrac{4 \times \boxed{}}{5 \times \boxed{}} = \dfrac{\boxed{}}{\boxed{}} = \boxed{}\%$

EXAMPLE 3 **Finding a Percent of a Number**

Find 20% of 55.

20% of 55 = 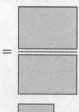   Write percent as a fraction and multiply.

$= \dfrac{\boxed{}}{\boxed{}}$ Use rule for multiplying fractions. Divide out common factor.

$= \boxed{}$ Multiply.

In Exercises 5–8, write the fraction as a percent.

5. $\frac{7}{25}$	6. $\frac{11}{20}$	7. $\frac{9}{10}$	8. $\frac{13}{50}$
9. Find 30% of 400.		**10.** Find 75% of 280.	

EXAMPLE 4 Using Percents

Soccer According to the Smithville Athletic Club, 47 of the 100 children playing Pee Wee Soccer this year are boys. What percent of the players are girls?

Solution

You know that $\frac{47}{100}$ = ▢ % of the soccer players are boys. To find the percent of soccer players who are girls, use the fact that the entire group of players represents 100%.

▢ % − ▢ % = ▢ %

Answer: ▢ % of the Pee Wee soccer players are girls.

Homework

Guided Practice Solve the following problem.

11. Of the 100 members of the school orchestra, 38 play string instrume
What percent of the members *do not* play string instruments?

Percents and Proportions

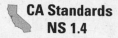
Goal: Use proportions to solve percent problems.

Solving Percent Problems

You can represent "*a* is *p* percent of *b*" with the proportion

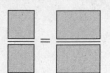

where *a* is part of the base *b* and *p*%, or $\frac{p}{100}$, is the percent.

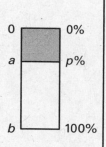

EXAMPLE 1   **Finding a Percent**

What percent of 4 is 3?

$$\frac{a}{b} = \frac{p}{100}$$ Write proportion.

 $= \dfrac{p}{100}$ Substitute ▢ for *a* and ▢ for *b*.

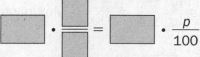 $\cdot \dfrac{p}{100}$ Multiply each side by ▢.

▢ = ▢   Simplify.

Answer: 3 is ▢ % of 4.

> In a percent [probl]em, the word that [follo]ws "of" is usually the base *b*.

1. What percent of 25 is 10?	**2.** What percent of 300 is 9?

3. In a grocery store, 6 of the 30 breakfast cereals are generic brand. What percent of the breakfast cereals are generic brand?

EXAMPLE 2 **Finding a Part of a Base**

Tennis 328 fans attended a tennis tournament. In a survey, 25% of the fans wanted players to wear traditional white tennis clothes. How many fans wanted players to wear traditional white clothing?

$$\frac{a}{b} = \frac{p}{100}$$ Write proportion.

$$\frac{\boxed{}}{\boxed{}} = \frac{\boxed{}}{100}$$ Substitute $\boxed{}$ for b and $\boxed{}$ for p.

$$\boxed{} \cdot \frac{\boxed{}}{\boxed{}} = \boxed{} \cdot \frac{\boxed{}}{100}$$ Multiply each side by $\boxed{}$.

$$\boxed{} = 328 \cdot \frac{\overset{1}{\boxed{}}}{\underset{\underset{1}{4}}{100}}$$ Use rule for multiplying fractions. Divide out common factors.

$$\boxed{} = \boxed{}$$ Multiply.

Answer: In the survey, $\boxed{}$ of the fans wanted players in traditional white clothing.

✓ **Check:** 25% of 328 is about $\frac{1}{4}$ of 300, or about 75. So, 82 is reasor

4. What number is 85% of 120?	**5.** What number is 7% of 200?
6. What number is 21% of 80?	**7.** What number is 62% of 900?

EXAMPLE 3 **Finding a Base**

48 is 40% of what number?

$$\frac{a}{b} = \frac{p}{100}$$ Write proportion.

$$\frac{\boxed{}}{\boxed{}} = \frac{\boxed{}}{100}$$ Substitute $\boxed{}$ for a and $\boxed{}$ for p.

 $\boxed{} = \boxed{}$ Cross products property.

$\dfrac{\boxed{}}{\boxed{}} = \dfrac{\boxed{}}{\boxed{}}$ Divide each side by $\boxed{}$.

$\boxed{} = \boxed{}$ Simplify.

Answer: 48 is 40% of $\boxed{}$.

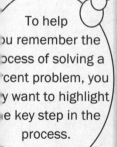

To help you remember the process of solving a percent problem, you may want to highlight the key step in the process.

nework

8. 21 is 42% of what number?	**9.** 39 is 60% of what number?

Formula Triangle

For practicing notetaking skills

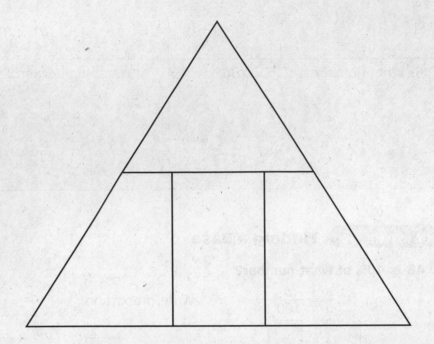

Percents and Decimals

Goal: Solve percent problems involving decimals.

EXAMPLE 1 **Writing Percents as Decimals**

a. 52% = .52%

= [　]

b. 4% = .04%

= [　]

c. 18.4% = .18.4%

= [　]

EXAMPLE 2 **Writing Decimals as Percents**

a. 0.27 = .27

= [　]

b. 0.03 = .03

= [　]

c. 0.091 = .091

= [　]

Guided Practice Write the percent as a decimal or the decimal as a percent.

1. 30%	**2.** 7%	**3.** 17.4%
4. 0.043	**5.** 0.01	**6.** 0.169

EXAMPLE 3 **Multiple Choice Practice**

Mary saves $\frac{5}{9}$ of her paycheck. What percent of her paycheck does Mary save?

(A) 23%   (B) 50%   (C) 55.6%   (D) 80%

Solution

$\frac{5}{9} \approx$ Divide 5 by 9. Round to the nearest thousandth.

=   Write as a percent.

Answer: Mary saves about [   ] % of her paycheck. The correct ans

is [ ] . (A) (B) (C) (D)

EXAMPLE 4 **Rewriting Small and Large Percents**

Video Store A video store carries 0.8% of their videos in foreign languag
The store increased their inventory of DVDs by 500%. Write these perce
as decimals.

Foreign language: 0.8% = **0**0.8%   DVDs: 500% = 500%

= [   ]   = [   ]

> You can also use equivalent fractions to write 0.8% as a decimal.
>
> $0.8\% = \frac{0.8}{100} = \frac{8}{1000}$
>
> $= 0.008$

Guided Practice **Write the fraction as a percent. Round to the nearest
of a percent.**

7. $\frac{1}{6}$	8. $\frac{7}{9}$	9. $\frac{6}{7}$	10. $\frac{9}{13}$

Write the percent as a decimal.

11. 0.36%	12. 740%	13. 0.0026%	14. 0.08%

EXAMPLE **5** **Using Percents**

Chemistry A chemical solution in a container has a volume of 85,000 milliliters. The solution contains 0.04% saline. How much of the solution is saline?

Solution

0.04% of 85,000 = [   ]   Write percent as a decimal.

= [   ]   Multiply.

Answer: The solution contains [   ] milliliters of saline.

WATCH OUT!

...lying a number ...percent less than ... results in a ...er less than the ...al number.

...lying by a percent ...er than 100% ...s in a number ...er than the ...al.

Guided Practice **Solve the following problem.**

...mework

15. The enrollment at Little Angel's Preschool last year was 50 students. This year's enrollment is 220% of last year's. How many students enrolled this year?

The Percent Equation

Goal: Use equations to solve percent problems.

The Percent Equation

You can represent "*a* is *p* percent of *b*" with the percent equation

[ ]

where *a* is part of the base *b* and *p*% is the percent.

EXAMPLE 1 **Finding a Part of a Base**

Pharmacy The pharmacy has 75% of the 300 tablets that Dr. Cole prescribed for her patient. How many tablets does the pharmacy have

Solution

$a = p\% \cdot b$ Write percent equation.

$= \boxed{}\% \cdot \boxed{}$ Substitute $\boxed{}$ for *p* and $\boxed{}$ for *b*

$= \boxed{} \cdot \boxed{}$ Write percent as a decimal.

$= \boxed{}$ Multiply.

Answer: The pharmacy has $\boxed{}$ of the tablets.

> As in fraction problems, "of" means to multiply. So, 75% of 300 means 0.75 X 300.

Guided Practice Use the percent equation to answer the question.

1. What number is 30% of 250?	**2.** What number is 32% of 65?

EXAMPLE 2 **Finding a Base**

The number 80 is 32% of what number?

$a = p\% \cdot b$ Write percent equation.

$\boxed{} = \boxed{}\% \cdot b$ Substitute $\boxed{}$ for a and $\boxed{}$ for p.

$\dfrac{\boxed{}}{\boxed{}} = \dfrac{\boxed{} \cdot b}{\boxed{}}$ Write percent as a decimal. Then divide each side by $\boxed{}$.

$\boxed{} = \boxed{}$ Simplify.

Answer: The number 80 is 32% of $\boxed{}$.

EXAMPLE 3 **Finding a Percent**

72 is what percent of 240?

In Example 3, you can use common percents to check the reasonableness of the answer. You know that 50%, or $\frac{1}{2}$, of 240 is 120. Because 72 is less than 50% of 240, 30% seems reasonable.

$a = p\% \cdot b$ Write percent equation.

$\boxed{} = p\% \cdot \boxed{}$ Substitute $\boxed{}$ for a and $\boxed{}$ for b.

$\dfrac{\boxed{}}{\boxed{}} = \dfrac{p\% \cdot \boxed{}}{\boxed{}}$ Divide each side by $\boxed{}$.

$\boxed{} = p\% = \boxed{}\%$ Simplify fraction. Then write as a percent.

Answer: The number 72 is $\boxed{}$% of 240.

Guided Practice Use the percent equation to answer the question.

3. 30 is 250% of what number?	**4.** 99 is what percent of 396?

EXAMPLE 4 **Finding a Commission**

> **Jewelry** A jewelry salesperson sells a bracelet for $350. The salesperson earns an 8% commission on the sale. How much is the commission?
>
> **Solution**
>
> $a = p\% \cdot b$ Write percent equation.
>
> $= \boxed{} \% \cdot \boxed{}$ Substitute $\boxed{}$ for p and $\boxed{}$ f
>
> $= \boxed{} \cdot \boxed{}$ Write percent as a decimal.
>
> $= \boxed{}$ Multiply.
>
> **Answer:** The commission is $\boxed{}$.

Guided Practice Solve the following problem

5. Ryan receives a 12% commission for selling furniture. Today he sells chair and ottoman for $595. How much is the commission?

Formula Triangle

For use with homework

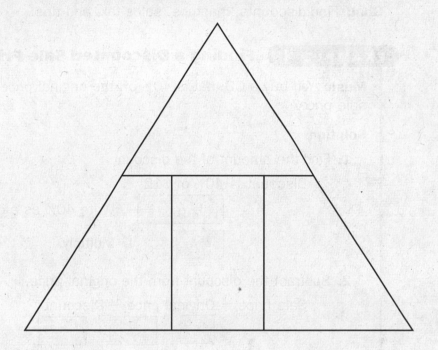

Discounts, Markups, Tips, and Sales Tax

CA Stand
NS 1.

Goal: Find discounts, markups, sales tax, and tips.

EXAMPLE 1 **Finding a Discounted Sale Price**

Music You buy a CD that is 40% off the original price of $12. What is th
sale price?

Solution

1. Find the amount of the discount.

Discount = 40% of $12

= [＿＿＿]   Write 40% as a decimal.

= [＿＿＿]   Multiply.

2. Subtract the discount from the original price.

Sale price = Original price − Discount

= [＿＿] − [＿＿] = [＿＿]

Answer: The sale price is $[＿＿].

EXAMPLE 2 **Finding a Markup**

Furniture A furniture store that sells sofas buys them from a manufactu
at a wholesale price of $350. The store's markup is 200%. What is the
price of the sofa?

1. Find the amount of the markup.

Markup = 200% of $350

= [＿＿＿]   Write 200% as a decimal.

= [＿＿]   Multiply.

2. Add the markup to the wholesale price.

Retail price = Wholesale price + Markup

= [＿＿] + [＿＿] = [＿＿]

Answer: The retail price is $[＿＿].

WATCH OUT!
In Example 2, do not
stop after multiplying
2.00 × 350. You
have to add the result,
$700, to the wholesale
price to get the retail
price.

1. A store is selling all shoes at 20% off the original price. What is the sale price of a pair of shoes originally priced at $65?

2. A store buys software from a manufacturer at a wholesale price of $72. The store's markup is 75%. What is the retail price?

EXAMPLE 3 **Multiple Choice Practice**

Diner At a diner, Maddie orders a meal that costs $8. She leaves a 15% tip. What is the total cost of the meal?

A $1.20   **B** $6.80   **C** $8.15   **D** $9.20

Solution

1. Find the tip.   15% of $8 = ⬚ = ⬚

2. Add the food bill and tip.   ⬚ = ⬚

Answer: The total cost of the meal is $ ⬚ .

The correct answer is ⬚ .   **A** **B** **C** **D**

EXAMPLE 4 **Solve a Multi-Step Problem**

Sales Tax A portable CD player that originally costs $80 is on sale fo
15% off. Find the total cost of the CD player if it has a 6% sales tax.

Solution

Step 1 **Find** the amount of the discount.

Discount = ☐ % of $ ☐ = ☐ = ☐

Step 2 **Subtract** the ☐ from the ☐ to find th
sale price.

Sale price = ☐ = ☐

Step 3 **Find** the sales tax on the sale price.

Sales tax = ☐ % of $ ☐ = ☐ = ☐

Step 4 **Add** the ☐ to the ☐ to find the total co:

Total cost = ☐ = ☐

Answer: The total cost of the CD player is $ ☐ .

Guided Practice **Solve the following problems.**

3. At a café, Ruthie orders soup, salad, and a drink that costs a total of
$7. Find the total cost of the meal if she leaves an 18% tip.

Homework

4. In Example 4, suppose the original price of the CD player is $90. Find
total cost of the CD player with a 15% discount and a 6% sales tax.

Simple Interest

Goal: Calculate simple interest.

Vocabulary

Interest:

Principal:

Simple interest:

Annual interest rate:

Balance:

Simple Interest

Words Simple interest *I* is the product of the [____] *P*, the

[_____] *r* written as a decimal, and the [____] *t* in years.

Algebra [____]

Numbers A $1000 deposit earns 5% simple annual interest for 3 years.

$$I = (\quad)(\quad)(\quad) = \$ \quad$$

EXAMPLE 1 **Multiple Choice Pratice**

Carol deposits $30 in a bank account that pays 5% simple annual inte
What will be the total amount that she has in the account after
2 years?

   Ⓐ $1.50   **Ⓑ** $31.50   **Ⓒ** $33   **Ⓓ** $150

$I = Prt$ Write simple interest formula.

$= \left(\boxed{}\right)\left(\boxed{}\right)\left(\boxed{}\right)$ Substitute $\boxed{}$ for P, $\boxed{}$ for r, and

                      for t.

$= \boxed{}$ Multiply.

To find the balance, add the interest to the principal.

Answer: Carol will have $30 + $$\boxed{}$, or $$\boxed{}$ in her account.

The correct answer is $\boxed{}$.   **Ⓐ**   **Ⓑ**   **Ⓒ**   **Ⓓ**

EXAMPLE 2   **Finding an Interest Rate**

You deposit $750 into an 8 month certificate of deposit. After 8 month
the balance is $770. Find the simple annual interest rate.

To find the interest, subtract the principal from the balance.

$\boxed{} - \boxed{} = \boxed{}$

Then use the simple interest formula and solve for r.

$I = Prt$ Write simple interest formula.

$\boxed{} = \left(\boxed{}\right)\left(\boxed{}\right)\left(\boxed{}\right)$ Substitute $\boxed{}$ for I, $\boxed{}$

                   and $\boxed{}$ for t.

$\boxed{} = \boxed{}$ Multiply.

$\dfrac{\boxed{}}{\boxed{}} = \dfrac{\boxed{}}{\boxed{}}$ Divide each side by $\boxed{}$.

$\boxed{} = \boxed{}$ Simplify.

$\boxed{}\% = \boxed{}$ Write decimal as a percent.

Answer: The simple annual interest rate is $\boxed{}$%.

WATCH OUT!

When using the simple interest formula, make sure you write the number of months as a fraction of a year. For example, 7 months should be written as $\frac{7}{12}$.

---

1. If you deposit $1500 into an account that earns 5% simple annual interest, what will the account's balance be after 4 months?

2. You deposit $800 into a 9 month certificate of deposit. After 9 months the balance is $848. Find the simple annual interest rate.

EXAMPLE 3 **Finding an Amount of Time**

Mario borrows $500 from a bank to pay for car repairs. His simple annual interest rate is 10%. Mario pays a total of $100 in interest on the loan. How long did Mario have the loan?

$$I = Prt$$ Write simple interest formula.

$$\left(\boxed{}\right) = \left(\boxed{}\right)\left(\boxed{}\right)\boxed{}$$ Substitute $\boxed{}$ for I, $\boxed{}$ for P, and $\boxed{}$ for r.

$$\boxed{} = \boxed{}$$ Multiply.

$$\dfrac{\boxed{}}{\boxed{}} = \dfrac{\boxed{}}{\boxed{}}$$ Divide each side by $\boxed{}$.

$$\boxed{} = \boxed{}$$ Simplify.

Answer: Mario had the loan for $\boxed{}$.

work

Formula Triangle

For use with homework

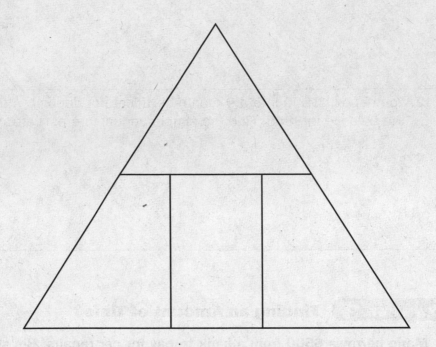

Words to Review

Give an example of the vocabulary word.

Percent

Percent equation

Interest

Principal

Simple interest

Annual interest rate

Balance

Review your notes and Chapter 6 by using the Chapter Review on pages 339–342 of your textbook.

Sampling Methods

CA Stand
SDAP
SDAP

Goal: Identify and compare sampling methods and recognize how a metho may create a biased sample.

Vocabulary

Population:

Sample:

Biased sample:

EXAMPLE 1 **Comparing Samples**

Lunch Survey You want to find out how many times in a 5-day school week students buy their lunch. You survey two homerooms.

a. Identify the population and the samples.

b. Suppose all homerooms are surveyed and the mean for the student population is buying lunch 3 times per week. Compare this mean with the means for the samples.

Buying Lunch	
Homeroom A	**Homeroom**
0, 0, 0, 0, 0	0
1, 1, 1	1
2, 2, 2, 2	2
3, 3, 3, 3	3, 3, 3, 3
4, 4, 4	4, 4, 4, 4, 4, 4,
5	5, 5, 5, 5, 5

Solution

a. The population is   . There

two samples: the students in   and the

students in   .

b. The mean number of times students buy lunch in a 5-day schoo

week is [ ] for Homeroom A and [ ] for Homeroom B. Comp

with a population mean of 3, students in Homeroom A bought

their lunch [ ] and students in Homeroom B bought their

lunch [ ].

---

1. Suppose you survey another homeroom. Below are the number of times they buy lunch each week. Compare the mean for Homeroom C with the population mean.
Homeroom C: 0, 0, 1, 1, 2, 2, 3, 3, 3, 3, 3, 3, 4, 4, 4, 4, 5, 5, 5, 5

Sampling Methods

In [   ], each person or object in a population has an equally likely chance of being selected.

In systematic sampling, a [   ] is used to select members of a population.

In [   ], easy to reach members of a population are selected.

In self-selected sampling, members of a population [   ] to be part of the sample.

EXAMPLE 2 **Identifying Sampling Methods**

Art Survey You survey artists about their favorite type of art material. Identify the sampling method. Tell whether the sample is likely to be biased.

a. Survey every other person entering an art class.

b. Survey every other person in a sculpture class.

Solution

a. This is [   ] sampling. The sample is probably [   ].

b. This is [   ] sampling. The sample is [   ] because the members of a sculpture are [   ] to favor sculpting material.

You survey students about their favorite sport. Identify

sampling method. Tell whether the sample is likely to be biased.

2. Survey the first 10 students in line at lunch.

3. Place a questionnaire in the school newspaper.

EXAMPLE 3 **Multiple Choice Practice**

**A researcher conducts a survey asking what type of public transpor
they use the most. Which of the following methods is the best way
the researcher to choose a representative sample?**

(A) Survey people waiting at a bus stop.

(B) Survey every tenth person who called for a taxi at a taxi-cab com

(C) Place a survey in the newspaper so that people can mail in their resp

(D) Survey by calling every 100th phone number in the phone book

Solution

Choices ▢ and ▢ are not representative samples because

people waiting for a bus or calling a taxi would tend to favor that type

transportation. Choice C asks people to volunteer, so it ▭

▭ .

Answer: The researcher should survey by ▭

▭ . The correct answer is ▢ .

(A) (B) (C) (D)

Homework

Sampling Errors

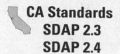

CA Standards
SDAP 2.3
SDAP 2.4

Goal: Identify sampling errors and bias and evaluate the validity of claims.

EXAMPLE 1 **Identifying Potentially Biased Questions**

Tell whether the question could produce biased results. If so, explain why and rewrite the question so that it is not biased.

Do you, like most people, prefer delicious chocolate milk?

Solution

A response of [   ] implies that the person disagrees with most people

and dislikes "delicious" chocolate milk. The question is [   ] because it

encourages a response of [   ] You could rewrite the question

as [   ]

EXAMPLE 2 **Claims Based on Biased Questions**

Randomly selected students were asked if they agree with the unreasonable dress code. The newspaper claims that most students oppose the dress code. Is the claim valid? Explain.

Solution

The claim may not be valid because the question is [   ]. The word

[   ] gives a negative opinion and encourages a response

of [   ]

Guided Practice **Tell whether the question could produce biased results. If so, explain why and rewrite the question so it is not biased.**

1. Do you support the construction of an unnecessary bridge?

EXAMPLE **3** **Claims Based on Biased Samples**

Travel You want to know about traveling among U.S. residents. You surve
people as they enter a travel station along the highway. The survey
question and results are displayed below. Is the given claim valid? *Explain*

Question: On average, how many times a year
do you travel out of state?

Claim: Most U.S. residents travel out of state
5 or more times a year.

Out-of-State Travel	
1–2	18%
3–4	30%
5 or more	52%

Solution

The claim may not be valid because ⬚⬚⬚⬚⬚⬚. People

entering a travel station are ⬚⬚⬚⬚ to travel than U.S. residents

general.

EXAMPLE **4** **Claims Based on Flawed Methods**

Pets You walk around the city park with your dog and survey people whe
they prefer dogs over cats. You find that 60% of the people you surveye
prefer dogs over cats. Is your claim valid? *Explain*.

Solution

The claim ⬚⬚⬚⬚⬚. Because your dog was with you while y

conducted your survey, ⬚⬚⬚⬚⬚⬚⬚

⬚⬚⬚⬚⬚.

Guided Practice **Solve the following problems.**

2. In Example 3, suppose the survey was conducted at a grocery store ra
than at a travel center. Is this sample likely to be biased? Explain.

Homework

3. In Example 4, describe a method for conducting the survey that mig
make the results and claim more likely to be valid.

Notetaking Organizer

For practicing notetaking skills

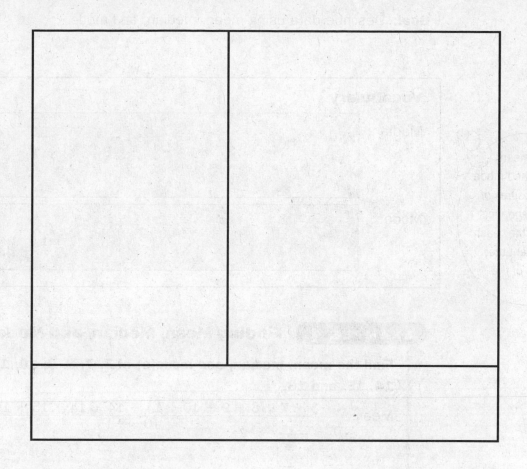

Mean, Median, and Mode

Goal: Describe data using mean, median, and mode.

> The mean, median, and mode are *measures of central tendency*, because they each represent the center of the data.

Vocabulary

Median:

Mode:

EXAMPLE 1 Finding Mean, Median, and Mode

Find the mean, median, and mode(s) of 3, 7, 8, 9, 10, 14, 14, 14, 15, and 16.

Mean: $\dfrac{3 + 7 + 8 + 9 + 10 + 14 + 14 + 14 + 15 + 16}{10}$

= ☐

= ☐

Median: The median is the mean of the two middle values, ☐ and

Median = ☐ = ☐ = ☐

Mode: The data value that occurs most often is ☐ .

EXAMPLE 2 **Multiple Choice Practice**

Casey found the mean and median of the numbers 2, 2, and 8. If the number 4 were added to the list of numbers, then

(A) the median would increase.   (B) the median would decrease.

(C) the mean would increase.   (D) the mean would decrease.

Solution

The new list of numbers is ⬜⬜⬜⬜⬜⬜. The mean of 2, 2, and 8 is

⬜ ÷ ⬜ = ⬜. If you add 4 to the list, the mean would still be 4, because

(⬜ + ⬜) ÷ ⬜ = ⬜.

The median of the original list is the middle value, ⬜. The median of the

new list is the mean of the two middle values, (⬜) ÷ ⬜ = ⬜.

So, the median would increase.

Answer: The correct answer is ⬜.   (A) (B) (C) (D)

Example 2,
mode is not
[affec]ted when you
[includ]e the number 4
[to the] list, because
[2] still occurs
[m]ost often.

Guided Practice **Find the mean, median, and mode(s).**

1. 6, 2, 7, 11, 2, 10, 5, 3, 8	**2.** 27, 63, 49, 34, 70, 58, 55, 68

3. In Example 2, suppose 2 were added to the list of numbers instead of 4. What would happen to the mean, median, and mode?

EXAMPLE 3 **Choosing a Useful Measure**

School Play The numbers of tickets sold for the upcoming school play are listed below. Which measure is most useful for describing a typical data value?

6 30 28 9 26 32 34 42 35 28 64 ⸻

Solution

The mean, ⬚ , is distorted by the largest number of tickets sold,

⬚ . So, most data values are ⬚ the mean. The mode, ⬚

is not typical because it is ⬚ most of the data values.

The median, ⬚ , represents the data values more closely.

Answer: The ⬚ is most useful for describing a typical

data value.

EXAMPLE 4 **Analyzing a Claim**

Pay Rates The pay rates for 12 employees at a company are shown ⸻ The company claims the average pay rate is $13. Does the claim des⸻ the prices well? Why might this pay rate be advertised?

$6, $7, $7, $8, $8, $9, $9, $13, $13, $13, $13, $14

Solution

The company's claim of $⬚ is the most common pay rate, or

⬚ . It does not describe the data well because it is

⬚ . This pay rate may be adver⸻

to suggest that the company ⬚ .

Guided Practice **Refer to Example 4 to solve the following problem.**

4. Which measure would be more accurate in describing a typical pay ra⸻

Homework

Range and Outliers

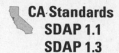
CA Standards
SDAP 1.1
SDAP 1.3

Goal: Analyze how the inclusion or exclusion of outliers affects measures of central tendency.

Vocabulary

Lower extreme:

Upper extreme:

Lower quartile:

Upper quartile:

Range:

Interquartile range:

Outlier:

Box-and-whisker plot:

EXAMPLE 1 **Computing Statistics**

Find the median, extremes, quartiles, range, and interquartile range o
the data set 22, 36, 24, 40, 18, 56, 33, 87, and 25.

Step 1 Order the data and identify the median and the extremes.

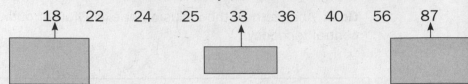

| 18 | 22 | 24 | 25 | 33 | 36 | 40 | 56 | 87 |

Step 2 Identify the quartiles using the lower and upper halves of the
data.

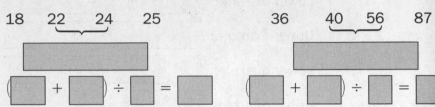

18   22   24   25   36   40   56   87

$$\left(\boxed{} + \boxed{}\right) \div \boxed{} = \boxed{} \qquad \left(\boxed{} + \boxed{}\right) \div \boxed{} = $$

Step 3 Subtract the extremes to find the range:

$$\boxed{} - \boxed{} = \boxed{}.$$

Step 4 Subtract the quartiles to find the interquartile:

range: $\boxed{} - \boxed{} = \boxed{}.$

> **WATCH OUT!**
> If a data set has an odd number of values, the median is not included in either the lower half or upper half.

EXAMPLE 2 **Describing Effects of Outliers**

Use the data set 59, 60, 64, 66, 68, 72, and 115. The data value 115
an outlier. How does the exclusion of the outlier affect the mean? *Exp*

Solution

Calculate the mean of the original data set.

Mean: $\boxed{} = \boxed{} = \boxed{}$

Then calculate the mean excluding the outlier $\boxed{}$.

Mean: $\boxed{} = \boxed{} \approx \boxed{}$

The mean $\boxed{}$ by about $\boxed{}$. The mean decreases because

outlier is the $\boxed{}$.

Guided Practice Use the data set 14, 12, 18, 15, 13, and 4.

---

1. Find the median, extremes, quartiles, range, interquartile range, and any outliers of the data set.

EXAMPLE 3 Using a Box-and-Whisker Plot

Test Scores The box-and-whisker plots below show the spread of the differences between the prices of winter coats at 25 stores in a mall. The data in the first plot have an outlier of $29. The second plot displays the same data but does not include the outlier. How does excluding the outlier affect the median and the range of the data?

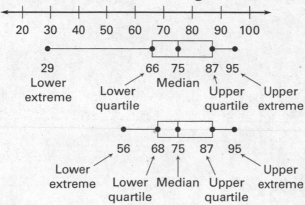

Solution

When the outlier is [ ], the median is [ ] and the range is [ ].

When the outlier is [ ], the median is [ ] and the range is [ ].

The median [ ] and the range greatly [ ] when the outlier is excluded.

Homework

Notetaking Organizer

For use with homework

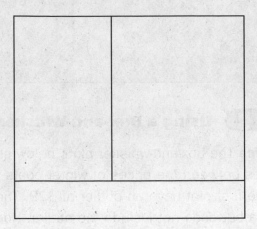

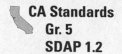

Histograms

Goal: Make and interpret histograms.

Vocabulary

Frequency table:

Frequency:

Histogram:

EXAMPLE 1   Making a Frequency Table

Auction The sellers on an Internet auction site tracked how many people viewed the auction each day. The data are listed below. Make a frequency table of the data.

15, 28, 36, 16, 18, 27, 40, 39, 25, 19, 36, 19, 42, 39,
27, 30, 49, 6, 27, 38, 0, 42, 37, 26, 17, 16, 25, 31, 29,
8, 10, 28, 34, 16, 9, 40, 32

Solution

1. Choose intervals of [ ] that cover all the data values, which range from [ ] to [ ]. In the table, each interval covers [ ] whole numbers. The first interval is [ ] and the last interval is [ ].

2. Make a [ ] next to the interval containing a given number of viewers of the auction.

3. Write the frequency for each interval by [ ] of tally marks for the interval.

CH OUT!
e that the
d interval
at 10, not 9,
se 9 can be in
ne interval.

Viewers	Tally	Frequency
10–19		
20–29		
30–39		

EXAMPLE 2 **Making a Histogram**

Phone Calls A business kept track of how many phone solicitors called them. The table shows the number of phone calls received each day. Make a histogram of the data.

Phone Calls	Tally	Frequency
0–4		8
5–9		0
10–14		12
15–19		18
20–24		9

Solution

1. Draw and label the [   ] and [   ] axes.

   List each interval from the frequency table on the [   ]

   The greatest frequency is [   ]. So, start the vertical axis at [   ]

   end it at [   ], using increments of 2.

2. Draw a bar for [   ]. The bars should have [   ] width.

   Include [   ] grid lines.

   Bars that are next to each other should [   ] gap between them.

> **WATCH OUT!**
>
> Make sure that your histogram includes all of the intervals in the table, even the intervals that have a frequency of 0.

1. The runs scored by the school baseball team in each game are listed below. Make a frequency table of the data.

2, 8, 0, 3, 5, 10, 2, 1, 3, 1, 0, 14, 2, 3, 5, 0, 6, 2, 12, 4, 8, 2

2. Make a histogram of the data in Exercise 1.

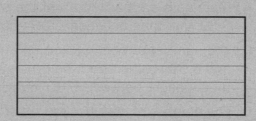

EXAMPLE 3 **Multiple Choice Practice**

Traffic Patterns City officials are looking at traffic patterns at a major intersection. They have tracked the average number of cars backed up at the stoplight between 5 A.M. and 6:59 P.M.

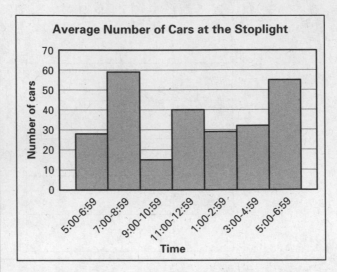

Which statement is *not* supported by these data?

(A) More cars are backed up at the stoplight between 5:00 A.M. and 8:59 A.M. than between 1:00 P.M. and 4:59 P.M.

(B) The number of cars backed up at the stoplight between 5:00 P.M. and 6:59 P.M. is about half the number of cars backed up at the stoplight between 5:00 A.M. and 6:59 A.M.

(C) The number of cars backed up at the stoplight is greatest during the times people would be traveling to and from work, and eating out for lunch.

(D) The number of cars backed up at the stoplight between 9:00 A.M. and 10:59 A.M. is about half the number of cars backed up at the stoplight between 3:00 P.M. and 4:59 P.M.

Solution

The number of cars backed up at the stoplight between 5:00 P.M. and

6:59 P.M. is about [   ]. The number of cars backed up at the stoplight

between 5:00 A.M. and 6:59 A.M. is about [   ].

Answer: The number of cars backed up at the stoplight between 5:00 P.

and 6:59 P.M. is about [   ] the number of cars backed up at the

stoplight between 5:00 A.M. and 6:59 A.M. The correct answer is [   ].

(A) **(B)** **(C)** **(D)**

Homework

Circle Graphs

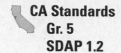

Goal: Use percents to make and interpret circle graphs.

Vocabulary

Circle graph:

Angle:

Vertex:

Degree:

EXAMPLE 1 **Interpreting a Circle Graph**

Class Survey The results of a survey are displayed in the circle graph. What are two conclusions you can make about the data?

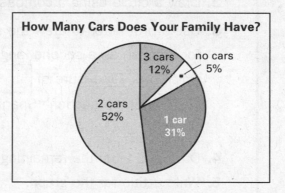

How Many Cars Does Your Family Have?

3 cars 12%

no cars 5%

2 cars 52%

1 car 31%

Solution

You can make conclusions about the data in the circle graph above.

en the data
ircle graph are
sed as fractions,
als or percents,
um of the data
ust be 1 or
100%.

- The largest section in the circle graph is labeled "   ." So, this is how many cars most families have.

- More families have "3 cars" than have "   cars."

EXAMPLE 2   **Making a Circle Graph Using Percents**

Second Language The table shows the results of a survey that asked students what second language they speak. Display the data in a circle graph.

Language	Percent
Spanish	30%
Vietnamese	25%
Portuguese	5%
None	40%

Solution

1. Find the angle measure of each section.

Section	Angle Measure				
Spanish	30% of 360° =		=		
Vietnamese	25% of 360° =		=		
Portuguese	5% of 360° =		=		
None	40% of 360° =		=		

2. Draw a circle using a compass. Mark its center.

3. Use a protractor to draw the angle for Spanish as a second language, which has a measure of ____. Then label the section "Spanish 30%."

4. Draw and label the remaining sections.

5. Write a title for the graph.

Need help using a compass? See page 682 of your textbook.

1. Can you determine from the circle graph the number of families that have three cars? Explain your reasoning.

2. The table shows the results of a survey that asked students to name their favorite pet. Display the data in a circle graph.

Pet	Percent
Dog	45%
Cat	30%
Rodent	15%
Amphibian	10%

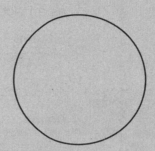

EXAMPLE 3 **Making a Circle Graph Using Data**

The table shows the results of a survey that asked people their favorite type of television show. Display the data in a circle graph.

Show	Sitcom	Drama	Cartoon	News
People	30	9	6	15

Solution

1. Find the total number of people surveyed.

$$30 + 9 + 6 + 15 = \boxed{}$$

2. To find the angle measure of each section, write each group of pe[ople] as a fraction of all the people and multiply by 360°.

Sitcom

$$\boxed{} = \boxed{} = \boxed{}$$

Drama

$$\boxed{} = \boxed{} = \boxed{}$$

Cartoon

$$\boxed{} = \boxed{} = \boxed{}$$

News

$$\boxed{} = \boxed{} = \boxed{}$$

3. Draw and label the circle graph.

Homework

Choosing and Analyzing Data Displays

CA Standards
SDAP 2.3
SDAP 2.5

Goal: Choose appropriate data displays and analyze the displays to make valid claims.

Appropriate Data Displays

- Use a [   ] to show how often each number occurs.

- Use a [   ] to display data in distinct categories.

- Use a [   ] to display data over time.

- Use a [   ] to represent data as parts of a whole.

- Use a [   ] to display how the data are spread out.

- Use a [   ] to compare the frequencies of data that fall in equal intervals.

EXAMPLE 1 **Choosing an Appropriate Data Display**

A movie theater manager wants to display the attendances to the movies shown in the theaters. What data display(s) should she use to see how the data are distributed, without displaying the individual data?

Answer: Either a [   ] or a [   ] will show how the data are distributed without showing individual data.

Guided Practice **Complete the following exercise.**

1. A bookstore sells eight different types of books. Which data display(s) should be used to compare the number of each type of book in stock?

EXAMPLE 2 **Making and Analyzing Line Graphs**

School The table shows the number of sixth-graders at your school from 2001 to 2004. Make two line graphs of the data, one with a break in the scale. Then make a conclusion based on each graph.

Sixth-Grade	
Year	**Num**
2001	6
2002	7
2003	8
2004	10

Step 1 **Think** of each pair of numbers in the table as an ordered pair: ([   ] , [   ]).

Step 2 **Choose** scales that include all the [   ].

Step 3 **Plot** [   ].

Step 4 **Draw** [   ] to connect the points.

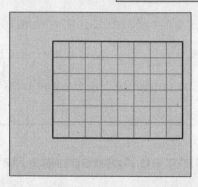 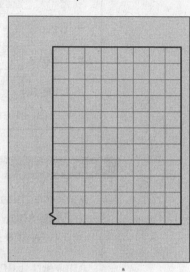

The symbol ⌇ on the vertical axis indicates that there is a break in the scale.

Step 5 **Analyze** each graph to make a conclusion.

From the first graph you can conclude that the number of sixth-graders [   ] from 2001 to 2004.

From the second graph, you can conclude the number of sixth-graders increased most rapidly from [   ].

EXAMPLE 3 **Evaluating Claims from Data Displays**

Annual Sales Tell whether the following claim is valid based on the line graph below. If not, make a valid claim.

Claim: The annual sales were steady from 2001 to 2003.

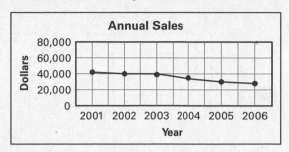

Solution

This claim is [   ]. The vertical axis uses [   ] increments, so

the graph is [   ]. So, it appears that sales remained

steady from 2001 to 2003. Sales actually [   ]. A valid claim is

that the [   ].

Guided Practice **Refer to Example 3 to solve the following problem.**

2. Redraw the line graph with smaller increments on the vertical scale. Compare the two graphs. What do you notice?

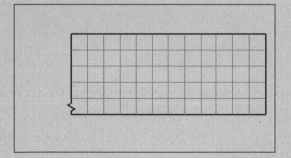

mework

Notetaking Organizer

For use with homework

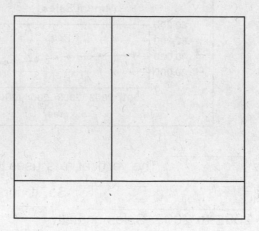

Words to Review

Give an example of the vocabulary word.

Population

Sample

Biased Sample

Median

Mode

Lower extreme

Upper extreme

Lower quartile

Upper quartile

Range

Interquartile range

Outlier

Box-and-whisker plot

Frequency table

Frequency

Histogram

Circle graph

Angle

Vertex

Degree

Review your notes and Chapter 7 by using the Chapter Review on pages 403–406 of your textbook.

Introduction to Probability

Goal: Represent probabilities as decimals and percents.

Vocabulary:

Outcomes:

Event:

Favorable outcomes:

Probability:

EXAMPLE 1 **Finding a Probability**

Find the probability of randomly choosing a striped ball from the balls shown at the right.

Because 5 out of 10 is 50% and there are 7 striped balls, the probability of choosing a striped ball must be greater than 50%.

Solution

$$P(\text{striped}) = \frac{\boxed{}}{\boxed{}}$$ ←——— There are [ ] striped balls.

←——— There are [ ] balls in all.

Answer: The probability of randomly choosing a striped ball is

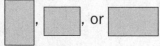 [ ], [ ], or [ ].

1. From the balls in Example 1, you randomly choose a spotted ball.

2. You get heads when you flip a coin.

EXAMPLE 2 **Multiple Choice Practice**

Hannah has 9 black, 4 pink, and 3 red purses in her closet. What is the probability that, without looking, she will pick a pink purse from her closet?

(A) 25%   (B) 30%   (C) 40%   (D) 50%

Solution

$P(\text{pink}) = \dfrac{\text{Number of favorable outcomes}}{\text{Total number of outcomes}}$

$P(\text{pink}) = $ [ ] ⟵ There are [ ] pink purses.

⟵ There are [ ] purses in all.

= [ ]   Simplify fraction.

= [ ]%   Write ratio as a percent.

The probability that Hannah will pick a pink purse is [ ]%.

Answer: The correct answer is [ ].   (A) (B) (C) (D)

EXAMPLE 3 **Making Predictions**

You roll a number cube 50 times. Predict the number n of rolls that will be an even number.

Solution

$\dfrac{\text{Number of even numbers}}{\text{Total number of outcomes}} = \dfrac{\text{Number of even numbers predicted}}{\text{Number of rolls}}$

[ ] = [ ]

[ ] = [ ]

[ ] = [ ]

Answer: You would expect to roll an even number [ ] times out of 50 rolls.

Because the probability of rolling an even number in 1 spin is $\frac{3}{6}$, the number of even numbers you can expect in 50 rolls is $\frac{3}{6}(50) = 25$.

nework

Experimental Probability

Goal: Find an experimental probability.

Vocabulary:

Theoretical probability:

Experimental probability:

EXAMPLE 1 **Finding an Experimental Probability**

Guests Robert tracked whether guests knocked on his door or rang his doorbell and wrote his results in the table at the right. Find the probability that the next guest will ring the doorbell.

Doorbell
Knock

1. Determine the number of successes and the number of trials.

Because a success is [_____], there

are [___] succeses.

There are [___] + [___] = [___] trials.

2. Find the probability.

$P(\text{doorbell}) = \dfrac{\boxed{}}{\boxed{}}$ ⟵ There are [___] successes.
  ⟵ There are [___] trials.

$= \dfrac{\boxed{}}{\boxed{}}$ Simplify.

Answer: The probability that the next guest will ring the doorbell is

[___], [_____], or [_____].

Guided Practice Solve the following problems.

1. In Example 2, what is the probability that the next guest will knock on the door?

2. At an auto dealership, of the last 150 vehicles purchased, 45 were sport utility vehicles. Find the probability that the next purchase will be a sport utility vehicle.

EXAMPLE 2 **Multiple Choice Practice**

> Predictions made based on probability are always estimates. Any prediction is *always* an estimate.

Cell Phones A survey of 150 twelve to seventeen year olds indicates that 48 of them have a cell phone. Which equation could you use to predict the number of twelve to seventeen year olds out of 1000 who have a cell phone?

(A) $\dfrac{48}{150} = \dfrac{1000}{x}$

(B) $\dfrac{48}{1000} = \dfrac{x}{150}$

(C) $\dfrac{48}{150} = \dfrac{x}{1000}$

(D) $\dfrac{150}{48} = \dfrac{x}{1000}$

Solution

You can solve the problem by using ratios to form a proportion.

$$\boxed{} = \boxed{}$$

$$\boxed{} = \boxed{}$$

Answer: You can solve $\boxed{} = \boxed{}$ to predict that $\boxed{}$ out of 1000

twelve to seventeen year olds have a cell phone. The correct answer is $\boxed{}$.

(A)   (B)   (C)   (D)

EXAMPLE **3** **Comparing Probabilities**

A spinner is divided into 6 equal parts, numbered 1 through 6. You spin the spinner 50 times. The results are shown in the table at the right. Compare the theoretical probability to the experimental probability of landing on a prime number.

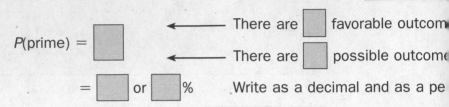

Number	1	2	3	4	5
Times landed on	9	8	7	7	9

Solution

Step 1 **Find** the theoretical probability of landing on a [   ]

$P(\text{prime}) = $ [   ] ⟵ There are [ ] favorable outcom

⟵ There are [ ] possible outcome

$= $ [   ] or [   ] %   Write as a decimal and as a pe

Step 2 **Find** the experimental probability of landing on a [   ]

$P(\text{prime}) = $ [   ] ⟵ There are [ ] successes.

⟵ There are [ ] trials.

$= $ [   ] or [   ] % Write as a decimal and as a prece

Answer: The experimental probability is [   ] the theoretical probability. The two probabilities will usually become closer with [   ] trials.

3. Based on your experiment, predict the number of times you will land in 150 spins.

Homework

4. Find the experimental probability of landing on a number greater tha Compare this to the theoretical probability of landing on a number g than 3.

Disjoint Events

CA Standards
SDAP 3.3
SDAP 3.4

Goal: Find the probability that either of two disjoint events occurs.

Vocabulary

Disjoint events:

Overlapping events:

Complementary events:

EXAMPLE 1 **Disjoint and Overlapping Events**

Tell whether the events involving the spinner are *disjoint* or *overlapping*.

Event P: Spin a number greater than 4.

Event Q: Spin an even number.

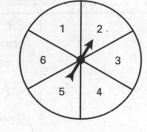

Solution

Make a list of the outcomes for each event. Then determine whether the events have any outcomes in common.

Event P: [   ] List the numbers greater than 4.

Event Q: [   ] List the even numbers.

Answer: There [   ] in common, so the events [   ].

Tell whether the events involving the spinner in Exampl

are *disjoint* or *overlapping*.

1. Event J: Spin a prime number.
Event K: Spin a number greater than 5.

Probability of Disjoint Events

Words For two disjoint events, the probability that either of the events

occurs is the [ ] of the probabilities of the events.

Algebra If A and B are disjoint events, then $P(A \text{ or } B) =$ [ ]

EXAMPLE 2 Multiple Choice Practice

Sierra has 4 red flowers, 3 pink flowers, and 3 white flowers in a bag. Sh
chooses 1 flower out of the bag without looking. What is the probability t
it will be pink or white?

(A) $\frac{2}{5}$ **(B)** $\frac{1}{2}$ **(C)** $\frac{3}{5}$ **(D)** $\frac{2}{3}$

Solution

Let event A be "choose pink" and event B be "choose white." The event
disjoint because they do not have any outcomes in common.

$P(A \text{ or } B) = P(A) + P(B)$ Events A and B are disjoint.

$= P(\boxed{}) + P(\boxed{})$ Identify Event A as $\boxed{}$

and Event B as $\boxed{}$.

$= \boxed{} + \boxed{}$ Find probabilities.

$= \boxed{}$ Add fractions.

$= \boxed{}$ Simplify.

Answer: The probability that the flower Sierra chooses is pink or
white is $\boxed{}$. The correct answer is $\boxed{}$.

(A) **(B)** **(C)** **(D)**

Copyright © by McDougal Littell, a division of Houghton Mifflin

EXAMPLE 3 **Probability of Complementary Events**

Day Care Of the workers at Kids Kingdom Day Care Center, 78% of the employees have professional certifications. What is the probability that a randomly chosen employee at the center is *not* certified?

Solution

P(not certified) = ☐ − P(certified)   Use complementary events.

= ☐ − ☐   Substitute ☐ %, or ☐ ,

= ☐   for P(certified).
Subtract.

Answer: The probability that a randomly chosen employee is not

certified is ☐ , or ☐ %.

Checkpoint   **Solve the following problems.**

2. In Example 2, what is the probability that Sierra will choose a red flower or a white flower?

3. Of the players on the baseball team, 88% are right-handed. What is the probability that a randomly chosen player is left-handed?

nework

Y Chart

For practicing notetaking skills

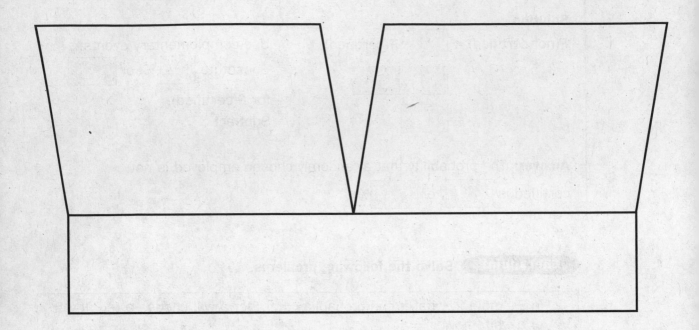

Compound Events

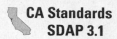
Goal: Use tree diagrams, tables, and grids to list outcomes and find probabilities.

Vocabulary

Compound event:

Tree diagram:

EXAMPLE 1 **Representing Outcomes**

Sandwich Shop For the daily sandwich special, you can choose ham or roast beef and you can choose Swiss cheese or cheddar cheese. How many choices of sandwiches are there?

Method 1

Make a table to list all possible choices of sandwiches.

	Swiss	Cheddar
Ham		
Roast beef		

Method 2

Make a tree diagram to list all possible choices of sandwiches.

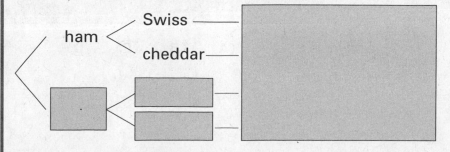

Answer: There are ⬜ different choices of sandwiches.

1. At a children's photography studio, parents can choose from pink, blue, black, or white for the background color and a rocking horse, a truck, or a doll for the prop. How many choices of photographs do parents have?

EXAMPLE 2 **Multiple Choice Practice**

Camp Scheduling You are scheduling your afternoon activities at camp. The activities are at 1:00 P.M. and 3:00 P.M., and the choices are craf rappelling, horseback riding, and music.

You must choose two different activities. Which set lists all possible aft noon activity schedules?

(A) R, M, C, H

(B) CR, CH, CM, RH, RM, HM

(C) CR, CH, RH, RM, HM, MC

(D) CR, CH, CM, RC, RH, RM, HC, HR, HM, MC, MR, MH

Solution

Because you must choose two different activities, do not include the sa activity in both schedules in the tree diagram.

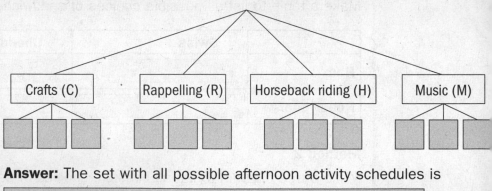

Answer: The set with all possible afternoon activity schedules is

. The corr

answer is . (A) (B) (C) (D)

Using a Tree Diagram

A sack has three chips in it: a red chip, a blue chip, and a green chip. To find the probability of randomly drawing the same chip when drawing a chip from the sack, replacing it, and drawing again, make a tree diagram to find the outcomes.

Solution

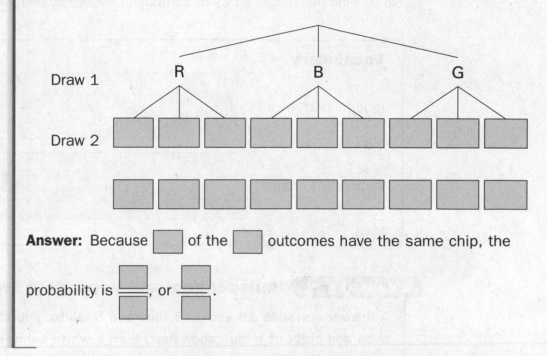

Draw 1

Draw 2

Answer: Because ▢ of the ▢ outcomes have the same chip, the

probability is $\dfrac{\square}{\square}$, or $\dfrac{\square}{\square}$.

Guided Practice Use a tree diagram to find the probability.

2. You roll a number cube and flip a coin. What is the probability that you roll a number greater than 4 and get heads?

mework

Independent and Dependent Events

Goal: Find the probabilities of compound events by using a formula.

Vocabulary

Independent events:

Dependent events:

EXAMPLE 1 **Independent and Dependent Events**

A drawer contains 15 socks, 7 blue and 8 white. You close your eyes and pull out a blue sock first, then a white sock, without replacing the blue sock. Are these events independent or dependent?

Whether or not you choose a blue sock first [   ] affect the likelihood you choose a white sock second. This is because the ratio of blue to wh socks in the drawer [   ] after the first sock is pulled from the d and not put back.

Answer: The events are [   ].

Guided Practice **A jar contains 8 red and 12 blue marbles.**

1. You randomly choose a marble, put it back, then randomly choose another marble. Are the events "choose a red marble first" and "choose a blue marble second" *independent* or *dependent*?

Probability of Independent Events

Words For two independent events A and B, the probability that both

events occur is the ⬚ of the probabilities of the events.

Algebra If A and B are independent events, then

$P(\text{A and B}) = $ ⬚ .

EXAMPLE 2 **Probability of Independent Events**

Carnival Tara is playing a game at a carnival where she picks a rubber duck from a pond. There are 12 ducks in the pond for which there is no prize and 4 ducks that will award a prize. What is the probability that Tara picks a prize-winning duck, replaces the duck in the pond, then picks another prize-winning duck?

> In common usage, being dependent means being free from the control of others. This help you remember the meaning of independent events.

Solution

1. Find the probability of each independent event.

$P(\text{win}) = \dfrac{}{} = $ ⬚   There are ⬚ ducks in all.

$P(\text{win}) = \dfrac{}{} = $ ⬚   Because Tara replaces the first duck, there are ⬚ winning ducks for the second pick.

2. Because the events are independent, multiply the probabilities.

$P(\text{win and win}) = $ ⬚

$= $ ⬚

$= $ ⬚

Answer: The probability that Tara selects 2 winning ducks from the pond in a row is ⬚ , or ⬚ %.

Probability of Dependent Events

Words For two dependent events, the probability that both events occur

is the ⬚ of the probability of the first event and the probability

of the second event ⬚ .

Algebra If A and B are dependent events, then

$P(\text{A and B}) = $ ⬚ .

EXAMPLE 3 · Probability of Dependent Events

Beverages Jeffrey's mother has 10 orange juice boxes, 7 grape juice boxes, and 3 lemonade juice boxes in the cooler for Jeffrey and his friends. Jeffrey randomly takes a juice box from the cooler, then randomly chooses another juice box without replacing the first. Find the probability that both juice boxes are grape.

Solution

Find the probability of the first event and the probability of the second e͏ given the first. Then multiply the probabilities.

1. $P(\text{grape}) = \boxed{}$ Out of $\boxed{}$ juice boxes, $\boxed{}$ a grape.

2. $P(\text{grape given grape}) = \boxed{}$ Of the remaining $\boxed{}$ juice box $\boxed{}$ are grape.

3. $P(\text{grape and grape}) = \boxed{}$ Multiply probabilities.

$= \boxed{}$ Divide out common factor.

$= \boxed{}$ Multiply.

Answer: The probability that both juice boxes are grape is $\boxed{}$.

> **WATCH OUT!**
> The probability of choosing a second grape juice box is $\frac{6}{19}$, not $\frac{7}{20}$, because the first juice box is not placed back into the cooler.

Guided Practice Refer to Example 3.

Homework

2. Find the probability that both juice boxes are lemonade when the fir͏ juice box chosen is not replaced.

Y Chart

For use with homework

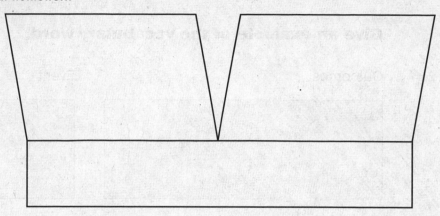

Words to Review

Give an example of the vocabulary word.

Outcomes

Event

Favorable outcomes

Probability

Theoretical probability

Experimental probability

Disjoint events

Overlapping events

Complementary events

Tree diagram

Compound events

Independent events

Dependent events

Review your notes and Chapter 8 by using the Chapter Review on pages 450–452 of your textbook.

Angles

Goal: Classify angles as complementary or supplementary and apply their properties.

Vocabulary

Acute angle:

Right angle:

Obtuse angle:

Straight angle:

Complementary:

Supplementary:

EXAMPLE 1 **Classifying Angles**

> A quick way to check the size of an angle is to use the corner of a piece of paper. Because the corner forms a right angle, it is easy to determine whether the angle's measure is less than 90°, exactly 90°, or greater than 90°.

Estimate the angle measure to classify the angle as *acute*, *right*, *obtuse*, or *straight*.

a.

G

b.

D

Solution

a. Because $m\angle G$ is _____ , $\angle G$ is _____ .

b. Because $m\angle D$ is _____ , $\angle D$ is _____ .

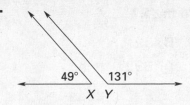

The angle above can be named in several ways: ∠ABC, ∠CBA, ∠B, and ∠1. Notice that the vertex must be in the middle or the only letter used in the name of the angle.

EXAMPLE 2 **Complementary and Supplementary Angles**

Tell whether the angles are *complementary*, *supplementary*, or *neither*.

a.

49°   131°
X Y

b.

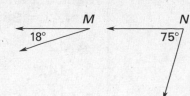

Solution

a. $m\angle X + m\angle Y =$ ☐ $+$ ☐ $=$ ☐ . So, ∠X and ∠Y are

☐ .

b. $m\angle M + m\angle N =$ ☐ $+$ ☐ $=$ ☐ . So, ∠M and ∠N are

☐ .

Guided Practice Classify the angle as *acute*, *obtuse*, *right*, or *straight*.

1. $m\angle D = 18°$	**2.** $m\angle V = 90°$	**3.** $m\angle S = 180°$	**4.** $m\angle J = 150°$

5. Give the measures of two angles that are complementary.

EXAMPLE 3 **Multiple Choice Practice**

For the two skateboard ramps at the right, ∠1 and ∠2 are complementary. If m∠1 = 38°, what is m∠2?

(**A**) 12°   (**B**) 52°

(**C**) 142°   (**D**) 322°

Solution

m∠1 + m∠2 = [ ]   Definition of [   ] angles

[ ] + m∠2 = [ ]   Substitute [ ] for m∠1.

m∠2 = [ ]   Subtract [ ] from each side.

Answer: The measure of ∠2 is [ ]. The correct answer is [ ].

(**A**)   (**B**)   (**C**)   (**D**)

Guided Practice Use the definitions of complementary and supplementa
angles to find the measure of the angle.

6. ∠P and ∠Q are supplementary. If m∠P = 98°, find m∠Q.

Homework

7. ∠T and ∠U are complementary. If m∠T = 16°, find m∠U.

Special Pairs of Angles

CA Standards
MG 2.1
MG 2.2

Goal: Identify special pairs of angles and lines.

Vocabulary

Adjacent angles:

Vertical angles:

Congruent angles:

Plane:

Intersecting lines:

Parallel lines:

Perpendicular lines:

Corresponding angles:

EXAMPLE 1 **Identifying Adjacent Angles**

Name all pairs of adjacent, supplementary angles.

Adjacent, supplementary angles:

EXAMPLE 2 **Using Vertical Angles**

Given that $m\angle 1 = 68°$, find $m\angle 3$.

You can also find $m\angle 3$ using supplementary angles. Apply the definition first to $\angle 1$ and $\angle 2$, and then to $\angle 2$ and $\angle 3$.

Because [ ] and $\angle 3$ are [ ] angles, they are [ ] .

So, $m\angle 3 =$ [ ] $=$ [ ] .

Guided Practice Refer to the diagram in Example 2.

1. Name all pairs of vertical angles.
2. Given that $m\angle 1 = 68°$, find $m\angle 2$.
3. Use your answer from Exercise 2 to find $m\angle 4$.

EXAMPLE 3 **Using Corresponding Angles**

Maps The map shows a section of Houston. Streets shown on maps often appear to form parallel or intersecting lines.

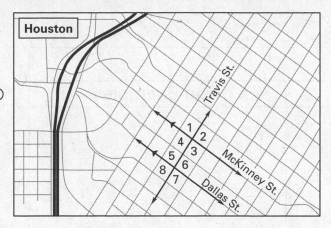

> **Arrowheads** e used to indicate that lines are parallel.

a. Name two streets that are parallel and two streets that intersect.

b. If $m\angle 1 = 85°$, find $m\angle 7$.

Solution

a. [_____] is parallel to [_____]. [_____]

intersects both [_____] and [_____].

b. Because $\angle$[__] and $\angle$[__] are [_____] angles,

[_____] = [_____] = [_____]. Because McKinney Street and Dallas Street

are [_____] lines, $\angle$[__] and $\angle$[__] are [_____]

angles. So, [_____] = [_____] = [_____].

Guided Practice Refer to the map in Example 3.

4. Find $m\angle 2$ and $m\angle 6$. Explain your reasoning.

nework

Examples and Non-Examples Chart

For practicing notetaking skills

Examples	Non-Examples

Triangles

CA Standards
MG 2.2
MG 2.3

Goal: Find unknown angles and draw triangles.

Vocabulary

Acute triangle:

Right triangle:

Obtuse triangle:

Congruent sides:

Equilateral triangle:

Isosceles triangle:

Scalene triangle:

Sum of the Measures of a Triangle

Words   The sum of the angle measures
of a triangle is _____.

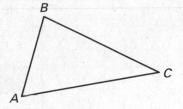

Algebra $m\angle \boxed{} + m\angle \boxed{} + m\angle \boxed{} = 180°$

EXAMPLE 1   **Finding an Angle Measure in a Triangle**

Find the value of x in the triangle shown.

$x° + \boxed{}° + \boxed{}° = \boxed{}°$ Sum of angle measures in a triangle is $\boxed{}$.

$x + \boxed{} = \boxed{}$ Add $\boxed{}$ and $\boxed{}$.

$x = \boxed{}$ Subtract $\boxed{}$ from each side.

Answer: The value of x is $\boxed{}$.

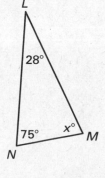

Triangles are named by their *vertices*. The vertices of the triangle in Example 1 are *L, M,* and *N,* so the triangle can be named with the notation △*LMN*. This notation is read "triangle *LMN*."

Guided Practice Find the value of *y*.

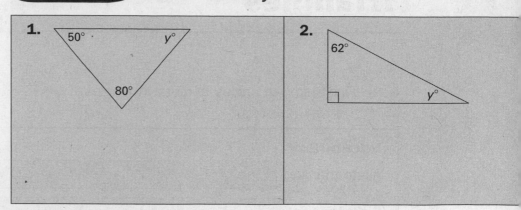

1.

50°   *y*°

80°

2.

62°

y°

EXAMPLE 2 **Multiple Choice Practice**

Which statement about the triangle is true?

(A) It is scalene.

(B) It is equilateral.

(C) It is isosceles.

(D) Its 3 angles are congruent.

5 cm   5 cm

2 cm

Solution

The triangle is not ⬜ because two sides are congruent. The tria

is not ⬜ because only two sides are congruent. The triangle

⬜ because two sides are congruent. The triangle does not ha

three congruent angles because it is not ⬜.

Answer: The correct answer is ⬜. (A) (B) (C) (D)

3.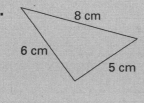

4.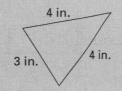

5.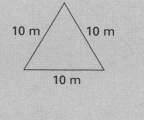

Classify the triangle by the lengths of its sides.

6.

7.

4 in.

3 in.   4 in.

8.

10 m   10 m

10 m

EXAMPLE 3 **Drawing Triangles**

Mosaic Draw a pattern for a tile in a mosaic in the shape of a right scalene triangle.

Solution

Step 1 Use a ruler to draw
and measure a

segment $\overline{AB}$

Step 2 Use a protractor
to draw a right

angle XAB as shown

Step 3 Draw point C on $\overrightarrow{AX}$ such that $AC \neq AB$. Then connect B and C.

mework

Quadrilaterals and Other Polygons

CA Standa
MG 2.3

Goal: Draw quadrilaterals from given conditions.

Vocabulary

Quadrilateral:

Trapezoid:

Parallelogram:

Rhombus:

Polygon:

Pentagon:

Hexagon:

Octagon:

Diagonal:

EXAMPLE 1   Drawing and Classifying a Quadrilateral

To help you classify quadrilaterals, you could draw a diagram that shows how the special quadrilaterals are related to each other.

Draw and classify a quadrilateral with opposite sides parallel, and all four sides of length 2 centimeters.

1. Draw two sides with a length of 2 centimeters. The angle between the two sides does not matter, except that it cannot be 0° or 180°.

2. Draw sides parallel to the first two sides to complete the figure.

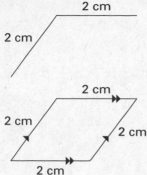

Answer: The figure is a ⬚.

Guided Practice   Sketch and classify the quadrilateral described.

1. A quadrilateral with 4 right angles, 4 congruent sides of length 3 centimeters, and both pairs of opposite sides parallel.

EXAMPLE 2   Finding Unknown Angle Measures

Find the value of *x* in the diagram shown.

Solution

The sum of the measures of the angles of a quadrilateral is ⬚. Write an equation involving *x* and then solve the equation.

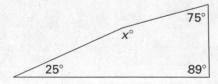

$x° + $ ⬚ $ + $ ⬚ $ + $ ⬚ $ = $ ⬚   **Write an equation.**

$x + $ ⬚ $ = $ ⬚   **Combine like terms.**

$x = $ ⬚   **Subtract** ⬚ **from each side.**

Answer: The value of *x* is ⬚.

2.

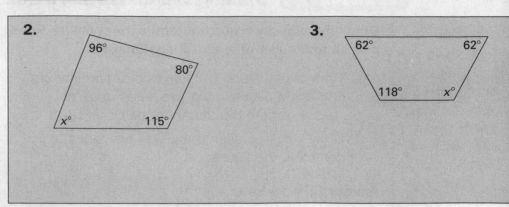

96°
80°
x° 115°

3.

62°   62°
118°   *x*°

EXAMPLE 3 **Angle Measures of a Regular Polygon**

a. Give the most specific name for the polygon.

b. Find the sum of the angle measures.

Solution

a. The polygon has _____ sides. All sides are

_____ and all angles are _____.

Answer: The polygon is a _____.

b. Draw all diagonals from one vertex. They

form _____ triangles.

Answer: The sum of the angle measures of

each of the 6 triangles is _____. The sum of

the angle measures of an octagon is _____ = _____.

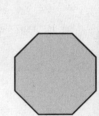

Homework

Examples and Non-Examples Chart

For use with homework

Examples	Non-Examples

CA Standa
NS 1.2

Similar and Congruent Polygons

Goal: Use ratios to show relative sizes of similar polygons.

Vocabulary

Similar polygons:

Congruent polygons:

Similar Polygons	**Congruent Polygons**
$\triangle LMN \sim \triangle PQR$	$\triangle ABC \cong \triangle DEF$

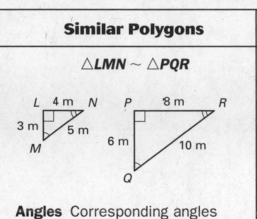

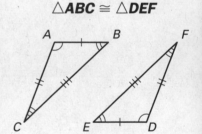

Angles Corresponding angles are congruent:

$\angle L \cong \angle\boxed{}$, $\angle M \cong \angle\boxed{}$,

and $\angle N \cong \angle\boxed{}$

Sides Ratios of lengths of corresponding sides are equal:

$$\dfrac{LM}{\boxed{}} = \dfrac{MN}{\boxed{}} = \dfrac{LN}{\boxed{}} = \boxed{}$$

Angles Corresponding angles are congruent:

$\angle A \cong \angle\boxed{}$, $\angle B \cong \angle\boxed{}$,

and $\angle C \cong \angle\boxed{}$

Sides Corresponding sides are congruent:

$\overline{AB} \cong \boxed{}$, $\overline{AC} \cong \boxed{}$,

and $\overline{BC} \cong \boxed{}$

EXAMPLE 1 **Finding Measures of Congruent Polygons**

Given that *ABCD* ≅ *WXYZ*, name the corresponding sides and corresponding angles. Then find *XY*.

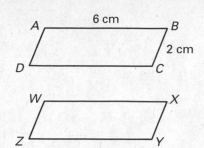

Solution

Corresponding Sides:

$\overline{AB}$ and [ ], $\overline{BC}$ and [ ],

$\overline{CD}$ and [ ], $\overline{AD}$ and [ ]

Corresponding Angles:

∠*A* and ∠[ ], ∠*B* and ∠[ ],

∠*C* and ∠[ ], ∠*D* and ∠[ ]

Because [ ] and $\overline{XY}$ are [   ] sides,

XY = [ ] = [ ] = centimeters.

Guided Practice Use the fact that △*ABC* ≅ △*LMN*.

1. Name the corresponding sides and corresponding angles.

   Corresponding Sides:

   Corresponding Angles:

2. Find the unknown angle measures.

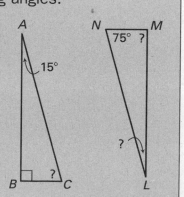

EXAMPLE **2** **Finding the Ratio of Lengths**

The ratios $\frac{DE}{AB}$, $\frac{EF}{BC}$, and $\frac{DF}{AC}$ are the ratios for the lengths of the corresponding sides of △DEF to △ABC in Example 2. Using these ratios, the ratio of the lengths of the corresponding sides is $\frac{3}{2}$.

Given that △ABC ~ △DEF, find the ratio of the lengths of the corresponding sides of △ABC to △DEF.

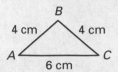

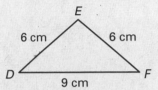

Write a ratio for each pair of corresponding sides. Then substitute the lengths of the sides and simplify each ratio.

$\dfrac{AB}{DE} = \boxed{} = \boxed{}$

$\dfrac{BC}{EF} = \boxed{} = \boxed{}$

$\dfrac{AC}{DF} = \boxed{} = \boxed{}$

Answer: The ratio of the lengths of the corresponding sides is $\boxed{}$.

EXAMPLE 3 **Checking for Similarity**

Landscape Design A landscape architect is planning a memorial garden at a local park. The rectangular garden will have a length of 216 inches feet and a width of 180 inches. A rectangular blueprint of the garden has a length of 12 inches and a width of 10 inches. Are the garden and the blueprint similar figures?

Solution

Because both figures are rectangles, all angles are ⬚ angles, so corresponding angles are ⬚ . To determine whether the figures are similar, see if the ratios of the lengths of the corresponding sides are ⬚ .

$$\frac{\text{Length of garden}}{\text{Length of } \rule{2cm}{0.3cm}} \stackrel{?}{=} \frac{\text{Width of } \rule{2cm}{0.3cm}}{\text{Width of } \rule{2cm}{0.3cm}}$$ Write ratios for lengths of corresponding sides.

$$\frac{\rule{3cm}{0.3cm}}{\rule{3cm}{0.3cm}} \stackrel{?}{=} \frac{\rule{3cm}{0.3cm}}{\rule{3cm}{0.3cm}}$$ Substitute.

$$\rule{3cm}{0.8cm} \quad \checkmark$$ Simplify.

Answer: The corresponding angles ⬚ and the ratios of the lengths of the corresponding sides ⬚ , so the figures ⬚ .

Guided Practice Solve the following problem.

3. In Example 3, suppose the blueprint is 10 inches long and 8 inches wide. Are the garden and the blueprint similar figures?

Using Proportions with Similar Polygons

Goal: Use proportions to find side lengths of similar polygons.

EXAMPLE 1 **Multiple Choice Practice**

Quadrilaterals *LMNO* and *PQRS* are similar. What is the length of $\overline{MN}$?

Ⓐ 4 cm   Ⓑ 17 cm

Ⓒ 14 cm   Ⓓ 32 cm

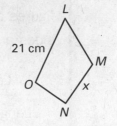

Solution

Use the ratios of the lengths of corresponding sides to write a proportio
involving the three known lengths and the unknown length.

$$\frac{LO}{\boxed{}} = \frac{MN}{\boxed{}}$$ Write proportion involving *MN*.

$$\frac{\boxed{}}{\boxed{}} = \frac{x}{\boxed{}}$$ Substitute known values.

$$\boxed{} = \boxed{}$$ Cross products property

$$\boxed{} = \boxed{}$$ Divide each side by $\boxed{}$.

Answer: The length of $\overline{MN}$ is $\boxed{}$ centimeters.

The correct answer is $\boxed{}$.   Ⓐ   Ⓑ   Ⓒ   Ⓓ

> Need help writing and solving proportions? See pages 266 and 274 of your textbook.

Guided Practice Find the unknown length *x* given that the polygons are similar.

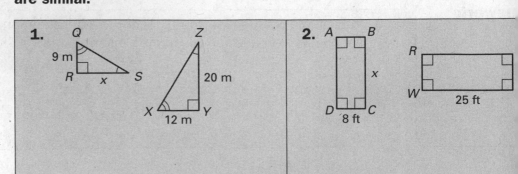

EXAMPLE 2 **Making an Indirect Measurement**

Flagpole A flagpole casts a shadow that is 25 feet long. Joe is 4 feet tall and casts a shadow that is 5 feet long. How tall is the flagpole?

Solution

You can use indirect measurement to find the height of the flagpole. Use the ratios of the lengths of the corresponding parts to write a proportion involving the unknown height h.

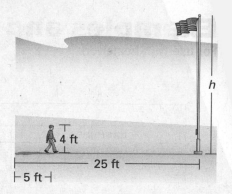

$$\frac{\text{Height of flagpole}}{\text{Joe's height}} = \frac{\text{Length of flagpole's shadow}}{\text{Length of Joe's shadow}}$$

$$\frac{\boxed{}}{\boxed{}} = \frac{\boxed{}}{\boxed{}}$$ Substitute known values.

$$\boxed{} \cdot \frac{\boxed{}}{\boxed{}} = \boxed{} \cdot \frac{\boxed{}}{\boxed{}}$$ Multiply each side by $\boxed{}$.

$$\boxed{} = \boxed{} \cdot \boxed{}$$ Simplify.

$$h = \boxed{}$$ Multiply.

Answer: The flagpole's height is $\boxed{}$ feet.

Guided Practice Use indirect measurement to solve the problem.

3. The shadow cast by a radio tower is 60 feet long. At the same time, the shadow cast by a 5-foot tall pole is 15 feet long. How tall is the radio tower?

nework

amples and Non-Examples Chart

se with homework

Examples	Non-Examples

Words to Review

Give an example of the vocabulary word.

Acute angle

Right angle

Obtuse angle

Straight angle

Complementary

Supplementary

Adjacent angles

Vertical angles

Congruent angles

Intersecting lines

Parallel lines

Perpendicular lines

Corresponding angles

Acute triangle

Right triangle

Obtuse triangle

Congruent sides

Equilateral triangle

Isosceles triangle

Scalene triangle

Quadrilateral

Trapezoid

Parallelogram

Rhombus

Polygon

Pentagon

Hexagon

Octagon

Diagonal

Similar polygons

Congruent polygons

Review your notes and Chapter 9 by using the Chapter Review on pages 503–506 of your textbook.

Converting Metric Units

Goal: Convert between metric units.

The metric system is a [_____]. Metric prefixes relate eac
unit to the base unit, such as meter, gram, or liter.

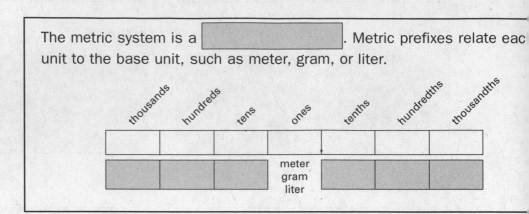

thousands   hundreds   tens   ones   tenths   hundredths   thousandths

meter
gram
liter

To convert between metric units n decimal places apart, [_____] or

[_____] as follows.

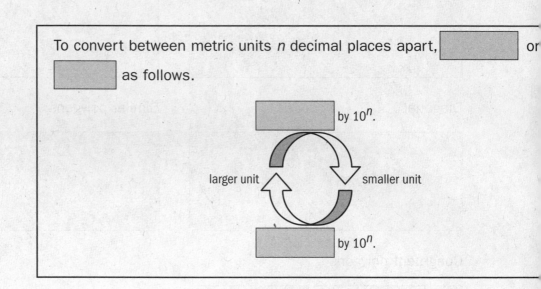

by 10^n.

larger unit   smaller unit

by 10^n.

EXAMPLE 1 **Converting Metric Units of Length**

The height of a chain-link fence is 137 centimeters. How many meters tall is the fence?

Solution

You are converting from a smaller unit ([   ]) to a larger unit ([   ]), so [   ] by a power of 10. Count the number of decimal places.

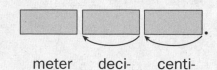

[ ]	[ ]	[ ] .
meter	deci-	centi-

From [   ] to [   ] , the decimal point is moved [   ] , so divide by [   ] , or [   ] .

137 ÷ [   ] = [   ]

137 centimeters = [   ] meters

Answer: The fence is [   ] tall.

EXAMPLE 2 **Converting Units of Mass and Capacity**

Copy and complete the statement.

a. 4620 g = __?__ kg   **b.** 27 L = __?__ mL

Solution

a. To convert from grams to kilograms, [   ] .

4620 ÷ [   ] = [   ] , so 4620 g = [   ] kg.

b. To convert from liters to milliliters, [   ] .

27 × [   ] = [   ] , so 27 L = [   ] mL.

1. 5600 m = __?__ km	**2.** 68 m = __?__ mm	**3.** 275 cm = __?__ m
4. 382 mm = __?__ cm	**5.** 500 g = __?__ kg	**6.** 1.75 kL = __?__ L

EXAMPLE 3 **Comparing Metric Measures**

Copy and complete the statement using <, >, or =.

    a. 650 cm __?__ 6 m   **b.** 1.6 kg __?__ 1525 g

Solution

To compare two measurements that have different units, convert one of the measures so that both have the same units.

    a. 650 cm __?__ 6 m   Strategy: Convert meters to ▢

       650 cm __?__ ▢ cm   6 × ▢ = ▢ , so 6 m = ▢

       650 cm ▢ ▢ cm   Compare.

Answer: 650 cm ▢ 6 m

    b. 1.6 kg __?__ 1525 g   Strategy: Convert kilograms to ▢

      ▢ g __?__ 1525 g   1.6 × ▢ = ▢ ,

                        so 1.6 kg = ▢ g.

      ▢ g ▢ 1525 g   Compare.

Answer: 1.6 kg ▢ 1525 g

7. 6.8 kL ___?___ 6725 L	**8.** 2.1 g ___?___ 2100 mg	**9.** 7.3 mm ___?___ 73 cm

EXAMPLE 4 **Solve a Multi-Step Problem**

Garden Beds Hank is planting a garden in his yard that is 8.5 meters long. Suppose the garden is divided into smaller beds that each measure 212.5 centimeters in length. How many small garden beds would there be?

Solution

1. Convert 8.5 meters to [   ] by multiplying by [   ].

   8.5 × [   ] = [   ] , so 8.5 m = [   ] .

2. To find the number of gardens, divide the [   ]

   by [   ] .

   [   ] cm ÷ [   ] cm = [   ]

Answer: The garden would be divided into [   ] smaller beds.

Guided Practice Solve the following problem.

10. In Example 4, suppose the garden were divided into beds that each measure 170 centimeters in length. How many small garden beds would there be?

mework

Converting Customary Units

Goal: Convert between U.S. customary units.

U.S. Customary Units of Measure

Length	Weight	Capacity

Length

1 ft = ☐ in.

1 yd = ☐ ft = ☐ in.

1 mi = ☐ yd = ☐ ft

Weight

1 lb = ☐ oz

1 T = ☐ lb

Capacity

1 c = ☐ fl oz

1 pt = ☐ c

1 qt = ☐ pt

1 gal = ☐ q

EXAMPLE 1 **Converting Customary Units of Length**

Farming The corn field on the Walters farm is made of 36 rows of the same length. Each row is 129 feet long. How many yards long is one ro of corn?

Solution

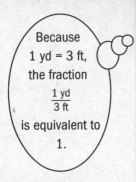

Because 1 yd = 3 ft, the fraction $\frac{1 \text{ yd}}{3 \text{ ft}}$ is equivalent to 1.

$129 \text{ ft} \times \dfrac{1 \text{ yd}}{3 \text{ ft}} = $ ☐

Use rule for multiplying fractio Divide out common factor and unit "ft".

$= $ ☐

Multiply.

Answer: A row of corn is ☐ yards long.

EXAMPLE 2 **Converting Customary Units of Weight**

African Elephants The weight of an average African elephant is 6 tons. How many pounds is this?

Solution

Use the fact that 1 T = 2000 lb.

$6 \text{ T} \times \dfrac{2000 \text{ lb}}{1 \text{ T}} =$ [ ]   Write 6 T as [ ].

$= $ [ ]   Use rule for multiplying fractions. Divide out common unit "T".

$= $ [ ]   Multiply.

Answer: The weight of an average African elephant is [ ] pounds.

EXAMPLE 3 **Multiple Choice Practice**

How many pints are in 36 fluid ounces?

Ⓐ $2\dfrac{1}{4}$ pints   Ⓑ $3\dfrac{3}{5}$ pints

Ⓒ 9 pints   Ⓓ 144 pints

Solution

$36 \text{ fl oz} \times \dfrac{1\text{c}}{8 \text{ fl oz}} \times \dfrac{1\text{pt}}{2\text{c}} =$ [ ]   Use rule for multiplying fractions. Divide out common factors and units.

$= $ [ ] , or [ ]   Multiply.

Answer: There are [ ] pints in 36 fluid ounces. The correct

answer is [ ] .   Ⓐ Ⓑ Ⓒ Ⓓ

Guided Practice **Copy and complete the statement.**

1. 2500 lb = __?__ T	**2.** 12 yd = __?__ in.	**3.** 9 c = __?__ fl oz

EXAMPLE 4 **Solve a Multi-Step Problem**

Convert 30 fluid ounces to cups and fluid ounces.

1. Convert 30 fluid ounces to cups.

$$30 \text{ fl oz} \times \frac{1 \text{ c}}{8 \text{ fl oz}} = \boxed{}$$

$$= \boxed{}, \text{ or } \boxed{}$$

2. Convert the fractional part from cups to fluid ounces.

$$\boxed{} = \boxed{}$$

$$= \boxed{}$$

Answer: So, 30 fl oz = $\boxed{}$ c $\boxed{}$ fl oz.

Guided Practice **Copy and complete the statement.**

4. 19 oz = ___?___ lb ___?___ oz	**5.** 9 pt = ___?___ qt ___?___ pt

---

EXAMPLE 5 **Adding and Subtracting with Mixed Units**

Animals Two puppies are in the veterinarian's office. The terrier weighs 18 pounds 9 ounces. The poodle weighs 12 pounds 13 ounces.

a. Find the sum of the weights. **b.** Find the difference of the weights

Solution

a. Add. Then rename the sum.

```
    18 lb    9 oz
  + 12 lb   13 oz
  _____
    ☐ lb  ☐ oz
    ☐ lb  ☐ oz  =  ☐ lb  ☐ oz
```

Answer: ☐ lb ☐ oz

b. Rename. Then subtract.

```
    18 lb   9 oz      ☐ lb  ☐
  − 12 lb  13 oz      ☐ lb  ☐
  _____
                      ☐ lb  ☐
```

Answer: ☐ lb ☐ oz

16 oz = 1 lb, so 22 oz is equal to 1 lb + 6 oz.

Homework

Converting Between Systems

Goal: Convert between systems.

Units of Measure		
Length	**Weight/Mass**	**Capacity**
1 in. = 2.54 cm	1 oz ≈ 28.35 g	1 fl oz ≈ 29.573 mL
1 ft = 0.3048 m	1 lb ≈ 0.454 kg	1 qt ≈ 0.946 L
1 mi ≈ 1.609 km		1 gal ≈ 3.785 L

EXAMPLE 1 **Converting Units of Measurement**

Copy and complete the statement. Round to the nearest whole number.

a. 54 cm ≈ __?__ in.   **b.** 31 fl oz ≈ __?__ mL

Solution

a. 54 cm × $\dfrac{1 \text{ in.}}{2.54 \text{ cm}}$ = ⬚ ≈ ⬚ ≈ ⬚

Answer: 54 cm ≈ ⬚

b. 31 fl oz × ⬚ = ⬚

= ⬚ = ⬚

Answer: 31 fl oz ≈ ⬚ mL.

EXAMPLE 2 **Comparing Measures**

Copy and complete using <, >, or =: 25 ft __?__ 7 m.

25 ft __?__ 7 m

[ ] m __?__ 7 m

[ ] m [ ] 7 m

Answer: 25 fl [ ] 7 m

Strategy: Convert feet to meters.

25 × [ ] = [ ]

so 25 ft = [ ] m

Compare.

Guided Practice Copy and complete the statement. Round to the neare_

whole number.

1. 3 mi ≈ __?__ km	**2.** 225 g ≈ __?__ oz	**3.** 2 L ≈ __?__ qt

Copy and complete the statement using <, >, or =.

4. 33 in. __?__ 85 cm	**5.** 20 oz __?__ 567 g	**6.** 2 gal __?__ 7 m

EXAMPLE **3**   **Converting Currency**

Use the exchange rate between U.S. dollars and Australian dollars shown in the graph.

a. A pack of pens costs 1.95 U.S. dollars. The same pack of pens costs 3 Australian dollars. In which country is the pack of pens cheaper?

b. About how many U.S. dollars are 15 Australian dollars worth?

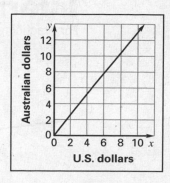

Solution

a. The graph shows that 3 Australian dollars are worth between ☐ U.S. dollars and ☐ U.S. dollars. The pack of pens is cheaper in ☐.

b. The graph shows that 13 Australian dollars are worth about $ ☐.

The exchange rate is ☐ Australian dollar ≈ $ ☐.

15 Australian dollars × ☐

= ☐

= ☐

15 Australian dollars are worth about ☐.

Guided Practice Copy and complete the statement using the exchange rate 1 U.S. dollar ≈ 11 Mexican pesos. Round to the nearest whole number.

7. $18 ≈ _?_ Mexican pesos	**8.** 355 Mexican pesos ≈ $ _?_

nework

Information Wheel

For practicing notetaking skills

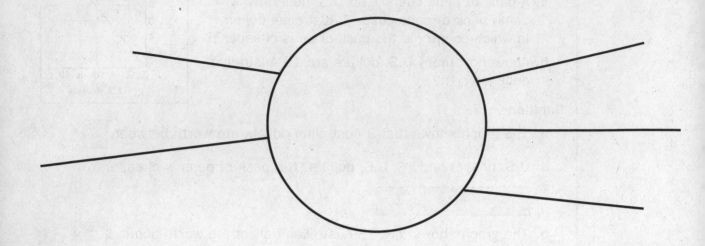

Area of a Parallelogram

CA Standards
AF 3.1
AF 3.2

Goal: Find the areas of parallelograms.

Vocabulary

Base of a parallelogram:

Height of a parallelogram:

Area of a Parallelogram

Words The area of a parallelogram is

the [ ] of a [ ] and the

corresponding [ ].

Algebra [ ] = [ ]

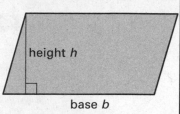

EXAMPLE 1 Finding the Area of a Parallelogram

Find the area of the parallelogram.

$A = bh$ Write formula for area.

= [ ]([ ])   Substitute [ ] for b and [ ] for h.

= [ ]   Multiply.

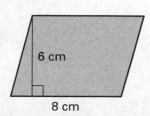

Answer: The area of the parallelogram is [   ].

WATCH OUT!
is measured
square units, not
units.

Guided Practice Find the area of the parallelogram with the given base b and height h.

1. $b = 12$ m, $h = 7$ m	**2.** $b = 7$ mm, $h = 7$ mm	**3.** $b = 10.5$ ft, $h = 8$ ft

EXAMPLE 2 **Finding the Base of a Parallelogram**

Glass Cutting A window in an office building is a parallelogram. The height of the window is 12 inches. The window covers 180 square inches. Find the base of the window.

Solution

$A = bh$ Write formula for area of a parallelogram

▢ $= b($ ▢ $)$ Substitute ▢ for A and ▢ for h.

▢ $=$ ▢   Divide each side by ▢ .

▢ $= b$ Simplify.

Answer: The base of the window is ▢ .

Guided Practice Find the unknown base or height of the parallelogram

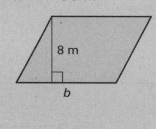

4. $A = 96 \text{ m}^2$

8 m

b

5. $A = 153 \text{ cm}^2$

h

17 cm

6. $A = 121 \text{ in.}^2$

h

11 in.

EXAMPLE 3 **Comparing Areas of Parallelograms**

A parallelogram has base 4 inches and height 2 inches. Its dimension doubled. Compare the areas of the original and enlarged parallelogra

Original parallelogram

2

4

Enlarged parallelogram

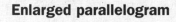

4

8

You can also compare the areas without finding the actual areas.
Original area: $A = bh$
Enlarged area:
$A = 2b \cdot 2h$
$= (2)(2)bh$
$= 4bh$

$A = bh$

$=$ ▢

$=$ ▢

$A = bh$

$=$ ▢

$=$ ▢

Answer: Because ▢ $=$ ▢ , the area of the enlarged parallelogram is ▢ times the area of the original parallelogram.

EXAMPLE **4** **Multiple Choice Practice**

A parallelogram with a base of 8 and a height of x is inside a parallelogram with a base of 14 and a height of 9, as shown. Which expression represents the area of the shaded region in terms of x?

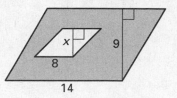

(**A**) $70 + 9x$ (**B**) $70 - 9x$

(**C**) $126 + 8x$ (**D**) $126 - 8x$

Solution

The area of the shaded region equals the area of the larger parallelogram ☐ the area of the smaller one. The area of the large parallelogram is $A = bh = $ ☐ $=$ ☐ . The area of the smaller parallelogram is $A = bh = $ ☐ . The area of the shaded region is ☐ .

Answer: The correct answer is ☐ .   (**A**)   (**B**)   (**C**)   (**D**)

Guided Practice   **Solve the following problem.**

mework

7. Suppose the dimensions of the original parallelogram in Example 3 are multiplied by 0.25. Compare the areas.

Areas of Triangles and Trapezoids

Goal: Find the areas of triangles and trapezoids.

Vocabulary

Base of a triangle:

Height of a triangle:

Bases of a trapezoid:

Height of a trapezoid:

Area of a Triangle

Words The area of a triangle is ☐ the product of a ☐

and the ☐ .

height

base b

Algebra ☐ = ☐

EXAMPLE 1 **Finding the Area of a Triangle**

Sculpture An artist is creating a sculpture that includes a triangular face that has a base 125 feet long and a height of 84 feet. Find the area of the triangular face.

84 ft

125 ft

Solution

$A = \frac{1}{2} bh$ Write formula for area of a triangle.

$= \frac{1}{2} \left(\boxed{} \right)\left(\boxed{} \right)$ Substitute ☐ for b and ☐ for h.

$= \boxed{}$ Multiply.

Answer: The area of the face is ☐ .

Finding the Base of a Triangle

A triangle has a height of 15 centimeters and an area of 202.5 square centimeters. Find the base of the triangle.

$A = \frac{1}{2} bh$ Write formula for area of a triangle.

[   ] = [   ]   Substitute [   ] for A and [   ] for h.

[   ] = [   ]   Simplify.

[   ] = b   Divide each side by [   ].

Answer: The base of the triangle is [   ].

Guided Practice **Find the unknown area or height of the triangle.**

1. $A = \underline{\ ?\ }$, $b = 7$ ft, $h = 12$ ft	**2.** $A = 52$ m^2, $b = 8$ m, $h = \underline{\ ?\ }$

Area of a Trapezoid

Words The area of a trapezoid is [   ] the product of the [   ] and the [   ].

Algebra [   ] = [   ]

Because a trapezoid has more than one base, the ses of a trapezoid are usually labeled b_1 and b_2. b_1 is read "b sub one."

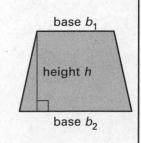

base b_1

height h

base b_2

EXAMPLE **3** **Finding the Area of a Trapezoid**

Find the area of the trapezoid shown.

$A = \frac{1}{2}(b_1 + b_2)h$ Write formula for area of a trapezoid.

$= \frac{1}{2}($ ▢ $+$ ▢ $)($ ▢ $)$ Substitute ▢ for b_1, ▢

for b_2, and ▢ for h.

$=$ ▢   Simplify.

8 in.

7 in.

3 in.

Answer: The area of the trapezoid is ▢ .

EXAMPLE **4** **Finding the Height of a Trapezoid**

A trapezoid has an area of 82 square meters. The bases are 11 meters and 9 meters. Find the height.

$A = \frac{1}{2}(b_1 + b_2)h$ Write formula for area of a trapezoid.

▢ $= \frac{1}{2}($ ▢ $+$ ▢ $)h$ Substitute ▢ for A, ▢ for b_1,

and ▢ for b_2

▢ $= \frac{1}{2}($ ▢ $)h$ Add.

▢ $=$ ▢ h Multiply.

▢ $= h$ Divide each side by ▢ .

Answer: The height of the trapezoid is ▢ .

Guided Practice Find the unknown area, base, or height of the trapezoid

3. $A = $ _?_ , $b_1 = 12$ ft, $b_2 = 8$ ft, $h = 4$ ft

Homework

4. $A = 22$ m^2, $b_1 = 7$ m, $b_2 = $ _?_ , $h = 4$ m

5. $A = 15$ cm^2, $b_1 = 3$ cm, $b_2 = 7$ cm, $h = $ _?_

Information Wheel

For use with homework

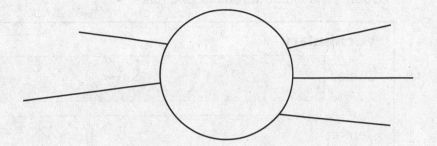

LESSON 10.6

Circumference of a Circle

CA Standa
MG 1.1
MG 1.2

Goal: Find circumferences of circles.

Vocabulary

Circle: _____

Center: _____

Radius: _____

Diameter: _____

Circumference: _____

Circumference of a Circle

Words The circumference of a circle is the product

of ▢ and the ▢, or ▢ the product

of ▢ and the ▢.

Algebra ▢ = ▢   ▢ = ▢

diameter *d*

radius *r*

EXAMPLE 1 **Finding the Circumference of a Circle**

Find the circumference of the sundial. Use 3.14 for π.

$C = \pi d$ Write formula for circumference.

$\approx$ ▢ (▢)   Substitute ▢ for π and

▢ for *d*.

$=$ ▢   Multiply.

Answer: The circumference of the sundial is about .

— 24 in. —

WATCH OUT!
The circumference of
a circle is measured
in linear units, not
square units.

EXAMPLE 2 **Finding the Circumference of a Circle**

When the radius or diameter of a circle visible by 7, use $\frac{22}{7}$ the approximation for π.

Find the circumference of the circle. Use $\frac{22}{7}$ for π.

$C = 2\pi r$ Write formula for circumference.

$\approx 2\left(\boxed{}\right)\left(\boxed{}\right)$ Substitute $\boxed{}$ for π and

$\boxed{}$ for r.

$= \boxed{}$ Multiply.

Answer: The circumference of the circle is about $\boxed{}$.

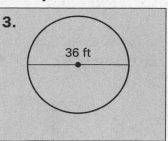

28 cm

Guided Practice   Find the circumference of the circle. Use $\frac{22}{7}$ or 3.14 for π.

1.

14 cm

2.

8 m

3.

36 ft

EXAMPLE 3 **Multiple Choice Practice**

A circular picture frame has a diameter of 9 centimeters. Which equation can be used to find its circumference, C, in centimeters?

A $C = 4.5 \times \pi$ **B** $C = 9 \times \pi$

C $C = 2 \times 9 \times \pi$ **D** $C = 9^2 \times \pi$

9 cm

Solution

$C = \boxed{}$ Write formula for circumference.

$= \pi\left(\boxed{}\right)$ Substitute $\boxed{}$ for d.

Answer: The equation $C = \boxed{}$, or $C = \boxed{} \times \boxed{}$, can be used to

find the circumference. The correct answer is $\boxed{}$.

Ⓐ Ⓑ Ⓒ Ⓓ

Guided Practice   Solve the following problem.

4. A DVD has a radius of 6 centimeters. Write an equation that can be used to find the circumference C (in centimeters) of the DVD.

EXAMPLE 4 **Finding the Diameter of a Circle**

Needlework Amelia is making a rug for her dining room floor. The rug
have a circumference of 44 feet. What will the diameter of the rug be

Solution

$$C = \pi d \qquad \text{Write formula for circumference.}$$

$$\boxed{} \approx \frac{22}{7}d \qquad \text{Substitute } \boxed{} \text{ for } C \text{ and } \frac{22}{7} \text{ for}$$

$$\boxed{}\left(\boxed{}\right) \approx \boxed{}\left(\frac{22}{7}\right)d \qquad \text{Multiply each side by } \boxed{}.$$

$$\boxed{} \approx d \qquad \text{Simplify.}$$

Answer: The diameter of the rug will be about $\boxed{}$.

Homework

Guided Practice   **Solve the following problem.**

5. The circumference of a circle is 100.48 meters. Find the circle's diam

Area of a Circle

CA Standards
MG 1.1
MG 1.2

Goal: Find the areas of circles.

Area of a Circle

Words The area of a circle is the product of ▢

and [   ].

Algebra ▢ = ▢

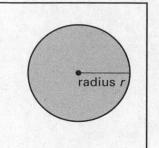
radius *r*

EXAMPLE 1 Finding the Area of a Circle

Find the area of the circle to the right. Use 3.14 for π.

$A = \pi r^2$ Write formula for area of a circle.

$\approx$ ([   ] [   ])   Substitute [   ] for π and

[ ] for *r*.

= [   ]   Simplify.

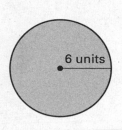
6 units

Answer: The area of the circle is about [   ].

EXAMPLE 2 Finding the Area of a Circle

Irrigation A farmer uses an irrigation system to water his crops. The diameter of the circle formed by the system is 54 feet. Find the area of the irrigated area.

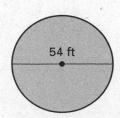
54 ft

Solution

1. Find the radius.

$r = \dfrac{d}{2} =$ [   ] = [   ] ft

2. Find the area.

$A = \pi r^2$ Write formula for area of a circle.

$\approx$ ([   ] [   ])   Substitute 3.14 for π and [   ] for *r*.

$\approx$ [   ]   Simplify.

Answer: The area of the irrigated area is about [   ].

Guided Practice Find the area of the circle. Use $\frac{22}{7}$ or 3.14 for π.

1.

12 m

2.

35 yd

3.

13 ft

EXAMPLE 3 **Multiple Choice Practice**

Which equation can be used to find the area A in square feet of a circl
with a radius of 14 yards?

(A) $A = 14 \times \pi$ **(B)** $A = 28 \times \pi$

(C) $A = \pi \times 14^2$ **(D)** $A = \pi \times 28^2$

Solution

$A = \pi r^2$ Write formula for area of a circle.

$= \pi \boxed{}$ Substitute $\boxed{}$ for r.

$= \pi \boxed{}$ Simplify.

Answer: The equation for the area of the circle is

$A = \boxed{}$, or $A = \boxed{}$. The correct answer is $\boxed{}$.

(A)   **(B)**   **(C)**   **(D)**

Homework

Information Wheel

For use with homework

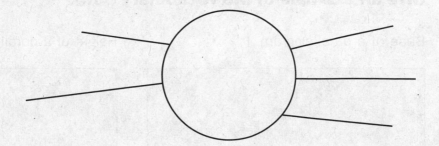

Words to Review

Give an example of the vocabulary word.

Base of a parallelogram

Height of a parallelogram

Base of a triangle

Height of a triangle

Bases of a trapezoid

Height of a trapezoid

Circle

Center

Copyright © by McDougal Littell, a division of Houghton Mifflin C

Radius

Diameter

Circumference

Review your notes and Chapter 10 by using the Chapter Review on pages 563–566 of your textbook.

Visualizing Solids

Goal: Classify and sketch views of solids.

Vocabulary

Solid:

Face:

Edge:

Vertex:

Prism:

Pyramid:

Cylinder:

Cone:

Sphere:

Cube:

EXAMPLE 1   Classifying Solids

Classify the solid as a *prism*, *pyramid*, *cylinder*, *cone*, or *sphere*.

a.

b.

c.

Solution

a. The baseball is a [   ].

b. The trunk is a [   ].

c. The water tower is a [   ].

Guided Practice   Classify the solid. Be as specific as possible.

1. 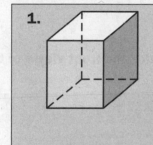	2. 	3. 

Lesson 11.1 • **Course 1 Notetaking Guide**   **241**

EXAMPLE 2 **Sketching Three Views of a Solid**

Sketch the top, side, and front views of the cylinder.

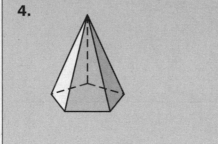

Solution

The top view of
a cylinder is
a ▢ .

The side view of
a cylinder is
a ▢ .

The front view
a cylinder is
a ▢

Guided Practice **Sketch the top, side, and front views of the pentagonal pyramid.**

4.

EXAMPLE **3** **Drawing Top, Side, and Front Views**

**Draw the top, side, and front views
of the solid shown at the right.**

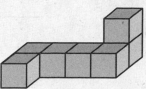

In the
solid at the
right, assume
are no hidden
es except those
orting the cubes
you can see.

Solution

1. To draw the top view, imagine
   what you would see if you
   were looking at the solid from
   directly above.

2. To draw the side view, imagine
   what you would see if you were
   looking directly at one of the
   sides.

3. To draw the front view,
   imagine what you would see if
   you were looking directly at
   the front.

Guided Practice **Draw the top, side, and front views of the solid shown.**

5.

nework

Surface Area of Prisms

Goal: Find the surface areas of prisms.

Vocabulary

Surface area:

Net:

EXAMPLE 1 **Finding Surface Area Using a Net**

Find the surface area of the rectangular prism.

1. Find the area of each face.

   Area of top or bottom: [ ] = [ ]

   Area of front or back: [ ] = [ ]

   Area of either side: [ ] = [ ]

> A *right prism* means that the edges connecting the bases are perpendicular to the bases.

8 in.

2 in.   8 in.   2 in.

3 in.

2. Add the areas of all six faces.

   [ ] = [ ]

Answer: The surface area of the prism is [ ].

Surface Area of a Rectangular Prism

Words The surface area of a rectangular prism is the [ ].

Algebra [ ] = [ ]

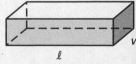

ℓ w

EXAMPLE 2 **Finding Surface Area Using a Formula**

Find the surface area of the rectangular prism.

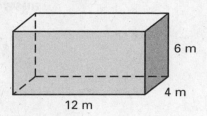

6 m

4 m

12 m

Solution:

$S = 2\ell w + 2\ell h + 2wh$ Write formula for surface area.

$= 2(\boxed{})(\boxed{}) + 2(\boxed{})(\boxed{})$ Substitute $\boxed{}$ for ℓ, $\boxed{}$ for

$+ 2(\boxed{})(\boxed{})$ w, and $\boxed{}$ for h.

$= \boxed{} + \boxed{} + \boxed{}$ Multiply.

$= \boxed{}$ Add.

Answer: The surface area of the prism is $\boxed{}$.

EXAMPLE 3 **Multiple Choice Practice**

The rectangular prism shown has length 10 centimeters, width 7 centimeters, and surface area S square centimeters. Which equation could be used to find the height h of the rectangular prism?

(**A**) $S = 34 + 2h$ (**B**) $S = 70 + 34h$

(**C**) $S = 140 + 34h$ (**D**) $S = 140 + 36h$

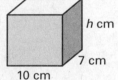

h cm

7 cm

10 cm

Solution

$S = 2\ell w + 2\ell h + 2wh$ Write formula for surface area.

$= 2(\boxed{})(\boxed{}) + 2(\boxed{})h + 2(\boxed{})h$ Substitute $\boxed{}$ for ℓ and

$\boxed{}$ for w.

$= \boxed{} + \boxed{}h + \boxed{}h$ Multiply.

$= \boxed{} + \boxed{}h$ Combine like terms.

Answer: The equation $\boxed{}$ could be used to find the

height. The correct answer is $\boxed{}$.   (**A**) (**B**) (**C**) (**D**)

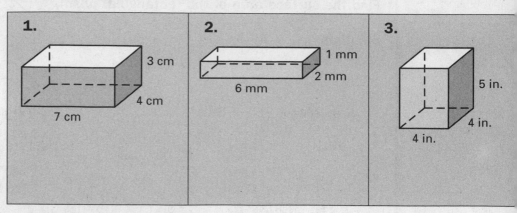

1.	2.	3.

1. 3 cm, 4 cm, 7 cm

2. 1 mm, 2 mm, 6 mm

3. 5 in., 4 in., 4 in.

EXAMPLE 4 **Finding Surface Area of a Triangular Prism**

Find the surface area of the triangular prism.

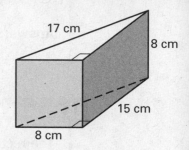

17 cm, 8 cm, 15 cm, 8 cm

Solution

1. **Find** the area of each face.

   Area of base: $\frac{1}{2} \times$ ☐ $\times$ ☐ $=$ ☐ cm²

   Area of square face: ☐ $=$ ☐ cm²

   Area of rectangular face: ☐ $=$ ☐ cm²

   Area of other rectangular face: ☐ $=$ ☐ cm²

2. **Add** the areas of all the faces.

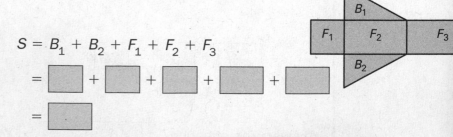

B_1, F_1, F_2, F_3, B_2

$S = B_1 + B_2 + F_1 + F_2 + F_3$

$ =$ ☐ $+$ ☐ $+$ ☐ $+$ ☐ $+$ ☐

$ =$ ☐

Answer: The surface area is ☐ .

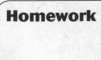

Homework

Surface Area of Cylinders

**CA Standards
AF 3.1**

Goal: Use the circumference formula to find surface areas of cylinders.

Surface Area of a Cylinder

Words The surface area of a cylinder is the

[____] of twice the area of a [____] and the

[____] of the base's [_____]

and [____].

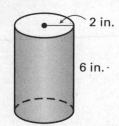

Algebra [____] = [_____]

EXAMPLE 1 **Finding the Surface Area of a Cylinder**

**Find the surface area of the cylinder at the
right. Use 3.14 for π.**

2 in.

6 in.

Solution

Use a net to find the surface area.

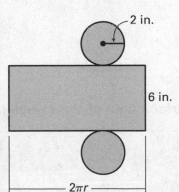

2 in.

6 in.

2πr

Area of base: $A = \pi r^2$

$\approx$ [____] [____] 2

= [____]

Area of curved surface:

$A = 2\pi rh$

$\approx 2($ [____] $)($ [____] $)($ [____] $)$

[____]

Surface area: $S =$ [____] + [____] + [____] = [____]

Answer: The surface area is about [_____].

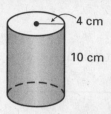

Finding Surface Area Using a Formula

Find the surface area of the cylinder. Use 3.14 for π.

4 cm

10 cm

Solution

$S = 2\pi r^2 + 2\pi rh$ Write formula.

$\approx 2(\boxed{})(\boxed{}) + 2(\boxed{})(\boxed{})(\boxed{})$ Substitute val

$= \boxed{} + \boxed{}$ Multiply.

$= \boxed{}$ Add.

Answer: The surface area is about $\boxed{}$.

Check: To check that your answer is reasonable, use 3 for π.

$S = \boxed{}(\boxed{})(\boxed{})^2 + \boxed{}\boxed{}(\boxed{})(\boxed{})$ Substitute val

$= \boxed{} + \boxed{}$ Multiply.

$= \boxed{}$ Add.

Because 336 is close to $\boxed{}$, a surface area of 351.68 cm^2

is $\boxed{}$.

Guided Practice **Find the surface area of the cylinder. Use 3.14 for π.**

1.

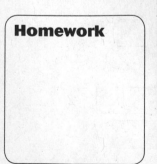

8 mm

2 mm

2.

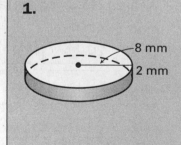

15 ft

6 ft

3.

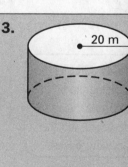

20 m

Homework

Four Square Diagram

For practicing notetaking skills

Definition:	Details:
Examples:	**Non-Examples:**

Volume of Prisms

Goal: Find the volumes of prisms.

Vocabulary

Volume: _____

Volume of a Prism

Words The volume of a prism is the _____

of the area of the _____ and the _____.

Algebra _____ = _____

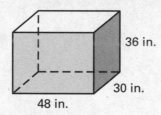

EXAMPLE 1 **Finding the Volume of a Rectangular Prism**

Freezer The Gilbert family has a chest freezer that has a length of 48 inches, a width of 30 inches, and a height of 36 inches. What is the volume of the freezer?

36 in.

30 in.

48 in.

Solution

$V = Bh$ Write formula for volume of a prism.

$= ($ _____ $)($ _____ $)$ Substitute (_____) for B, and _____

$= $ _____   Multiply.

Answer: The freezer will hold _____.

Guided Practice Find the volume of the rectangular prism.

1.	2.	3.
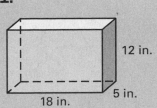 12 in. 5 in. 18 in.	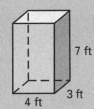 7 ft 4 ft 3 ft	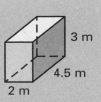 3 m 4.5 m 2 m

EXAMPLE 2 **Multiple Choice Practice**

The triangular prism shown at the right has volume *V* cubic inches. Which equation could be used to find the height *h* of the prism?

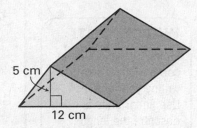

5 cm

12 cm

(A) $V = 17h$ (B) $V = 20h$

(C) $V = 30h$ (D) $V = 60h$

Solution

1. Find the area of the triangular base.

    $B =$ ☐ (☐)(☐) = ☐

2. Find the equation for the volume of the prism.

    $V = Bh$ Write formula for volume of prism.

    $=$ ☐h Substitute ☐ for *B*.

Answer: The equation ☐ could be used to find the height of the prism. The correct answer is ☐.

(A) (B) (C) (D)

Guided Practice Find the volume of the triangular prism.

4.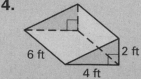

6 ft 2 ft
4 ft

5.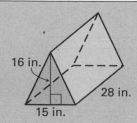

16 in.
28 in.
15 in.

6.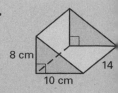

8 cm 14
10 cm

EXAMPLE 3 **Finding the Height of a Rectangular Prism**

The rectangular prism shown has a volume of 2052 cubic millimeters. Find the prism's height.

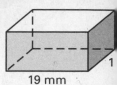

19 mm

Solution

$V = Bh$ Write formula for volume of a prism.

 $= ($ 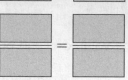 $)h$ Substitute [ ] for V, and ([ ]) for B.

[ ] = [ ]   Multiply.

$\dfrac{[\ ]}{[\ ]} = \dfrac{[\ ]}{[\ ]}$ Divide each side by [ ].

[ ] $= h$ Simplify.

Answer: The height of the prism is [ ].

Homework

Guided Practice Find the unknown length of the rectangular prism.

7. $V = 144$ ft^3, $\ell =$ _?_ , $w = 3$ ft, $h = 6$ ft

Volume of Cylinders

Goal: Find the volumes of cylinders.

Volume of a Cylinder

Words The volume of a cylinder is the [   ] of

the [   ] of the base and the [   ].

Algebra [   ] = [   ] = [   ]

EXAMPLE 1 **Finding the Volume of a Cyclinder**

What is the volume of the cylinder? Use 3.14 for π.

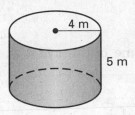

4 m

5 m

> You have learned any properties and formulas related to solids. Writing a summary of what you e learned may help ou prepare for the chapter test.

Solution

$V = \pi r^2 h$ Write formula for volume of a cylinder.

$\approx$ ([   ]) ([   ]) ([   ])   Substitute [   ] for π, [   ] for r, and [   ] for h.

= [   ]   Multiply.

Answer: The volume of the cylinder is about [   ].

Check: To check that your answer is reasonable, use 3 for π.

$V \approx$ ([   ]) ([   ])^2 ([   ])   Subsitute values.

= [   ]   Multiply.

Because 240 is close to [   ], a volume of 251.2 cubic meters is

[   ].

EXAMPLE 2 **Finding the Height of a Cylinder**

The cylindrical glass has volume of about 42.39 cubic inches. Find the height of the glass. Use 3.14 for π.

3 in.

h in.

Solution

The radius of the glass is half the diameter, or 1.5 inches.

$V = \pi r^2 h$ Write formula for volume of pri

$\boxed{} \approx \left(\boxed{}\right)\left(\boxed{}\right)^2 h$ Substitute values.

$\boxed{} \approx \boxed{}$ Multiply.

$\boxed{} \approx \boxed{}$ Divide each side by $\boxed{}$.

Answer: The height of the glass is about $\boxed{}$.

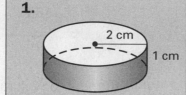

WATCH OUT!

Make sure to use the dimeter, in the formula for the volume of a cylinder.

Guided Practice Find the volume of the cylinder. Use 3.14 for π.

1.

2 cm

1 cm

2.

6 in.

9 in.

3.

8 m

6 m

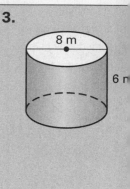

4. Find the height of a cylinder that has a radius of 7 inches and a volu of 1538.6 cubic inches. Use 3.14 of π.

EXAMPLE 3 **Multiple Choice Practice**

A hole in the shape of a rectangular prism is cut through a cylinder, as shown at the right. Which expression represents the volume of the solid in terms of the height h? Use 3.14 for π.

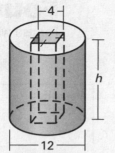

(A) 21.68h (B) 97.04h

(C) 105.04h (D) 436.16h

Solution

1. The volume of the cylinder is $\pi r^2 h \approx$ (⬚)(⬚)$h =$ ⬚ .

2. The volume of the hole is $Bh =$ (⬚) ⬚ $=$ ⬚ .

3. Find the ⬚ of the volumes: ⬚

   $=$ ⬚ .

Answer: The expression ⬚ represents the volume of the solid. The correct answer is ⬚ . (A) (B) (C) (D)

Guided Practice Solve the following problem.

5. In Example 3, suppose that the cylinder has a diameter of 6 and that the hole has a length of 2 and a width of 3. Write an expression for the volume of the solid in terms of the height h.

Four Square Diagram

For use with homework

Definition:	Details:
Examples:	Non-Examples:

Words to Review

Give an example of the vocabulary word.

Solid

Face

Edge

Vertex

Prism

Pyramid

Cylinder

Cone

Sphere

Surface area

Cube

Volume

Net

Review your notes and Chapter 11 by using the Chapter Review on pages 610–
of your textbook.

The Coordinate Plane

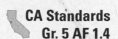

Goal: Identify and plot points in a coordinate plane.

Vocabulary

Coordinate plane:

x-axis:

y-axis:

Origin:

Quadrant:

Ordered pair:

x-coordinate:

y-coordinate:

Scatter plot:

EXAMPLE **1** **Naming Ordered Pairs**

Name the ordered pair that represents the point.

a. A **b.** B

Solution

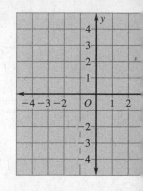

a. Point A is [ ] units to the [ ] of

the origin and [ ] units [ ]. So, the

x-coordinate is [ ] and the

y-coordinate is [ ]. Point A is

represented by the ordered pair $([\ ], [\ ])$.

b. Point B is [ ] units to the [ ] of the origin and [ ] unit [ ]

So, the x-coordinate is [ ] and the y-coordinate is [ ]. Point B

represented by the ordered pair $([\quad], [\quad])$.

EXAMPLE **2** **Multiple Choice Practice**

Which of the following points is located in Quadrant IV?

Ⓐ $P(2, -3)$ **Ⓑ** $Q(-4, 3)$ **Ⓒ** $R(1, 0)$ **Ⓓ** $S(-4$

> The notation $P(2, -3)$ means that point P is represented by the ordered pair $(2, -3)$.

Solution

Plot points P, Q, R, and S in a coordinate plane.

Point [ ] lies on the x-axis. Point [ ] is located

in Quadrant II. Point [ ] is located in Quadrant III.

Point [ ] is located in Quadrant IV.

Answer: Point [ ] is located in Quadrant IV. The correct answer

is [ ]. Ⓐ Ⓑ Ⓒ Ⓓ

Plot the point and describe its location.

1. $W(6, 1)$ **2.** $X(0, 4)$ **3.** $Y(-1, 3)$ **4.** $Z(-2, -4)$

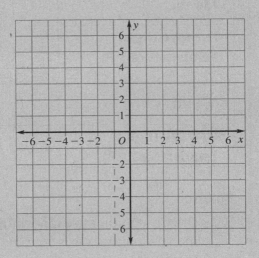

EXAMPLE 3   **Finding Segment Lengths and Area**

Find the length, width, and area of rectangle *ABCD* shown.

> Need help with
> absolute value? See
> pager 135 of your
> textbook.

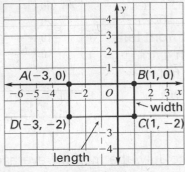

The length of the rectangle is the *horizontal* distance between *A* and *B*. To find this distance, find the absolute value of the difference between the *x*-coordinates of *A* and *B*.

Length = $|$*x*-coordinate of *A* − *x*-coordinate of *B*$|$

$\qquad$ = [ ] = [ ] = [ ] units

The width of the rectangle is the *vertical* distance between *A* and *D*. To find this distance, find the absolute value of the difference between the *y*-coordinates of *A* and *D*.

Width = $|$*y*-coordinate of *A* − *y*-coordinate of *D*$|$

$\qquad$ = [ ] = [ ] = [ ] units

The area of the rectangle is found by multiplying the length and width.

Area = ℓw = [ ] = [ ] square units

EXAMPLE **4**   **Making a Scatter Plot**

Average High Temperature The monthly average high temperatures in Myrtle Beach are listed in the table below. Make a scatter plot of the data. Then make a conclusion about the data.

Month	1	2	3	4	5	6
Average High Temperature (°F)	56	60	68	76	83	88

Month	7	8	9	10	11	12
Average High Temperature (°F)	91	89	85	77	69	60

Solution

1. Draw a coordinate plane with months on the *x*-axis and temperatures on the *y*-axis

2. Interpret each column of data as an ordered pair: (month temperature). Plot the ordered pairs in the table.

3. Look for a pattern. The points tend to rise from left to right from Month 1 to Month 7 and then fall from left to right from Month 7 to Month 12.

Monthly Average High Temperature in Myrtle Beach, SC

Because none of the data values are negative, you need to draw only the first quadrant of a coordinate plane

Homework

Answer: From January to July, the monthly average high temperature [   ] and from July to December, the monthly average high temperature [   ].

Functions and Equations

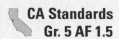

Goal: Write equations to represent linear functions.

Vocabulary

Function:

Input:

Output:

Domain:

Range:

EXAMPLE 1 **Evaluating a Function**

Evaluate the function $y = 3x$ **when** $x = 8$**.**

$y = 3x$ Write rule for function.

$-$ Substitute [ ] for *x*.

$=$ Multiply.

EXAMPLE 2 **Making an Input-Output Table**

Make an input-output table for the function $y = x - 5$ using the domain 0, 1, 2, and 3. Then state the range of the function.

Solution

Input x	0	1	2	3
Substitution	$y = \boxed{} - 5$	$y = \boxed{} - 5$	$y = \boxed{} - 5$	$y = \boxed{}$
Output y	$\boxed{}$	$\boxed{}$	$\boxed{}$	$\boxed{}$

The range of the function is the set of outputs: $\boxed{}$, $\boxed{}$, $\boxed{}$,
and $\boxed{}$.

Guided Practice Complete the following problem.

1. Make an input-output table for the function $y = 4 - x$ using the doma
−1, 0, 1, and 2. Then state the range of the function.

EXAMPLE 3 **Multiple Choice Practice**

Which equation shows the relationship between x and y?

Input x	−2	−1	0	1	2	3	4
Output y	−6	−3	0	3	6	9	12

A $y = x - 4$ **B** $x = y + 4$ **C** $y = 3x$ **D** $x = 3$

Solution

Compare each output value to its corresponding input value. Notice that
each output value is the input value $\boxed{}$. The equation
$\boxed{}$ shows the relationship.

Answer: The correct answer is $\boxed{}$.

EXAMPLE 4 **Solve a Multi-Step Problem**

Squares In the diagram of the squares, the input *s* is the length of each side of a square. The output *P* is the perimeter of the square. What is the perimeter of a square with sides 9 units?

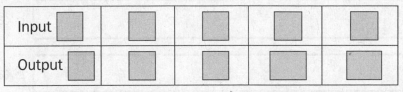

1 unit   2 units   3 units   4 units

Solution

1. Begin by making an input-output table.

Input					
Output					

2. Notice that each output value is ⬚ the input value. So, a rule for the function is ⬚.

3. To find the perimeter of a square with sides 9 units, evaluate the function when *s* = 9. Because $P = $ ⬚ $= $ ⬚, the perimeter of the square is ⬚.

Guided Practice Write a function rule for the input-output table.

2.

Input *x*	−1	0	1	2
Output *y*	−2	0	2	4

3.

Input *x*	2	4	6	8
Output *y*	3	5	7	9

mework

Definition and Examples Chart

For practicing notetaking skills

	Word and definition

	Example

	Example

	Example

Graphing Functions

Goal: Graph linear functions in a coordinate plane.

Vocabulary

Linear function:

> **EXAMPLE 1** **Graphing a Function**

Graph the function $y = 3x - 1$.

1. Make an input-output table by choosing several input values and evaluating the function for the output values.

2. Use the table to write a list of ordered pairs:

x	Substitution	y
−2		
−1		
0		
1		
2		

3. Plot the ordered pairs in a coordinate plane.

4. Notice that all of the points lie on a line. Any other ordered pair (x, y) that is a solution of the equation $y = 3x - 1$ also lies on the line when graphed. The line represents the complete graph of the function $y = 3x - 1$.

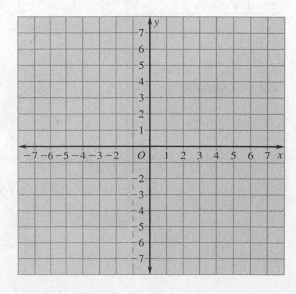

When the n of a function given, assume includes every e for which the n can produce orresponding y-value.

Graph the function.

1. $y = x - 2$	**2.** $y = -2x$	**3.** $y = 4x + 1$
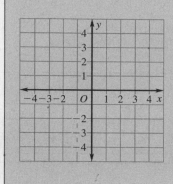	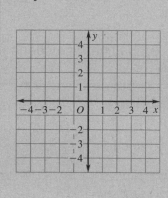	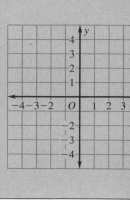

EXAMPLE 2 Writing and Graphing a Function

The cost of gasoline is $1.50 per gallon. Write and graph a function th
represents the cost *y* of *x* gallons of gasoline.

The situation can be represented with a table, a graph, and a function ru

1. Make an input-output table.

2. Plot the ordered pairs and connect them.

Input *x*	Output *y*
0	
1	
2	
3	
4	

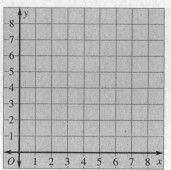

WATCH OUT!

In Example 2, note that you cannot have less than 0 gallons of gasoline, so you cannot use any numbers less than 0 in the domain.

Homework

3. Write a function rule. Notice that each output is [ ] times the in

value. A rule of the function is [ ]

Slope

CA Standards
Gr. 7 AF 3.3

Goal: Find the slope of a line.

Vocabulary

Slope:

EXAMPLE 1 **Finding the Slope of a Line**

To find the slope of a line, find the ratio of the rise to the run between two points on the line.

> Rise is positive when moving up and negative when moving down.

a.

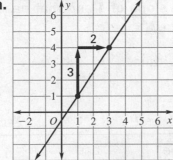

b.

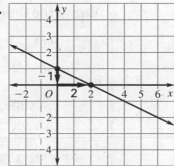

slope = $\frac{\text{rise}}{\text{run}}$ = ☐

slope = $\frac{\text{rise}}{\text{run}}$ = ☐ = ☐

EXAMPLE 2 **Interpreting Slope as a Rate**

Lemonade Stand The graph represents the cups of lemonade sold over time. To find the rate of sales, find the slope of the line.

slope = $\frac{\text{rise}}{\text{run}}$ = ☐   Rise from (0,0) to (2,8) is 8.
                                                Run from (0,0) to (2,8) is 2.

= ☐   Find unit rate.

Answer: The lemonade sold at a rate of

☐ cups per hour.

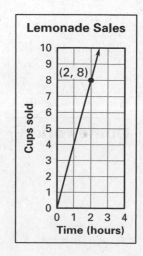

Lemonade Sales

---

1. Plot the points (1, 5) and (0, 8). Then find the slope of the line that
passes through the points.

2. In Example 2, suppose the line starts at the origin and passes throug
the point (2, 7). Find the rate of lemonade sales.

EXAMPLE 3   **Using Slope to Draw a Line**

Draw the line that has a slope of 4 and that passes through (2, 1).

1. Plot (2, 1).

2. Write the slope as a ratio.

slope = [ ] = [ ]

3. Move [ ] unit to the [ ] and

[ ] units [ ] to plot a second point.

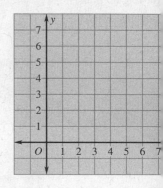

4. Draw a line through the two points.

Guided Practice Refer to Example 3.

3. Draw the line that has a slope of $-\dfrac{2}{3}$ and passes through (5, 4).

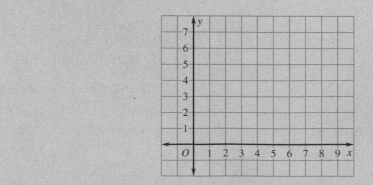

Homework

Definition and Examples Chart

For use with homework

	Word and definition
	Example
	Example
	Example

Words to Review

Give an example of the vocabulary word.

Coordinate plane

x-axis

y-axis

Origin

Quadrant

Ordered pair

x-coordinate

y-coordinate

Scatter plot

Function

Input

Output

Domain

Range

Linear function

Slope

Review your notes and Chapter 12 by using the Chapter Review on pages 651–654 of your textbook.